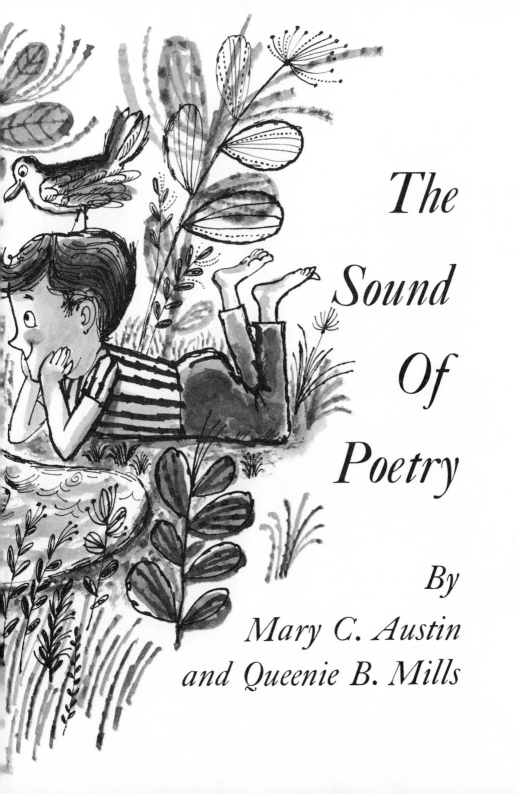

The

Sound

Of

Poetry

By

Mary C. Austin
and Queenie B. Mills

Artwork By

DON MADDEN

Acknowledgments

Grateful acknowledgment is made to authors, publishers, and others for their permission to include the following poems:

Abelard-Schuman Limited for "A Little Bird," "The Package," "Newspaper," "The Workshop," "Tummy-Ache," "Counting Sheep," "Puppy," "Fireflies," "The World's So Big," "Houses," "But That Was Yesterday," "A Picnic," "Snoring," and "Down in the Hollow" from *Up a Windy Hill* by Aileen Fisher, copyright 1953, by Aileen Fisher, copyright, 1933, 1938. Reprinted by permission of the publishers.

Abingdon Press for "Footwear" from *Winds A'Blowing* by May Justus, copyright, 1945, by Whitmore and Stone, 1961, by Abingdon Press.

American Boy for "Jack O'Lantern" by Anna Chandler Ayre. Reprinted by permission of the publishers.

American Junior Red Cross News and Eleanor Chaffee for "The Cobbler."

Louise Andrews for "The Purple Cow" by Gelett Burgess.

Appleton-Century-Crofts, Inc. for "Rain Riders" by Clinton Scollard from *St. Nicholas Magazine*, copyright, 1922, The Century Company; "The Little Elfman" by John Kendrick Bangs and "The Sea Princess" by Katherine Pyle from *St. Nicholas Book of Verse*, copyright, 1923, The Century Company; "The Elf and the Dormouse" from *Artful Antiks* by Oliver Herford; "Cicada Shell" by Basho from *A History of Japanese Literature* by W. G. Aston. Reprinted by permission of the publishers.

Association for Childhood Education International for "Good Morning" by Muriel Sipe Ross; "Fuzzy Wuzzy, Creepy Crawly" by Lillian Schulz Vanada and "In the Moonlight" by Norreys Jepson O'Conor from *Sung Under the Silver Umbrella*, copyright, 1935, The Macmillan Company, New York, N.Y., by permission of the Association for Childhood Education International.

Dorothy W. Baruch for "Merry-Go-Round," "Automobile Mechanics," "Barber's Clippers," and "Lawn Mower" from *I Like Machinery* by Dorothy W. Baruch; "Cat," and "Rabbits" from *I Like Animals* by Dorothy W. Baruch.

Beckley-Cardy Company for "Who Is Tapping at My Window?" by A. G. Deming.

The Viking Press, Inc. for "The Circus," "The Hens," "The Rabbit," "Mumps," "Little Rain," and "The People" from *Under the Tree* by Elizabeth Madox Roberts, copyright, 1922, by B. W. Huebsch, Inc., 1950, by Ivor S. Roberts; "My Dog" and "Shoes" from *In and Out* by Tom Robinson, copyright, 1943, by Tom Robinson. Reprinted by permission of The Viking Press, Inc.

Sara Ruth Watson for "Bouncing Ball."

Wee Wisdom for "A Story in the Snow" by Pearl R. Crouch.

Wells Gardner Darton and Company, Ltd. for "There Was a Lady of Niger" by Cosmo Monkhouse from *Another Book of Verse*.

Dixie Willson for "The Mist and All."

Yale University Press for "Watching Clouds" and "Chanticleer" from *Songs for Parents* by John Farrar.

Sharing Poetry
With Children

What is Poetry?

Poetry is the essence of an insight, a mood, an experience crystallized in language. The selection and arrangement of the words contribute to the statement and projection of this core of meaning, feeling, or sensory impression. Thus, the poet uses words much as an artist uses shapes and colors to capture, abstract, and express his interpretation or clarification of some experience. But poetry is also the sister art of music. It paints; but it also sings. Sometimes it even dances. Always it is an aesthetic experience which, as Robert Frost said, often "begins in delight and ends in wisdom."

There is, of course, no single, best answer to the question, "What is poetry?" And perhaps the only appropriate definition will remain forever embedded in the experiencing of poetry itself, either as creative endeavor or as aesthetic response. Certainly prose attempts are inadequate. Perhaps only the poet himself is capable of describing for us that special alchemy of thought and feeling which is poetry. Eleanor Farjeon, who has given us so many lovely poems for children, pictures it this way:

> What is poetry? Who knows?
> Not the rose, but the scent of the rose;
> Not the sky, but the light of the sky;
> Not the fly, but the gleam of the fly;
> Not the sea, but the sound of the sea;
> Not myself, but something that makes me
> See, hear and feel something that prose
> Cannot; what is it? Who knows?

Why Poetry for Young Children?

In this aerospace age with its increasing emphasis on science and mathematics, some people ask, "Why poetry for children?" and in particular, "Why poetry for *young* children?" It would be foolish indeed to pretend that poetry has the practical survival value that technology promises. Yet, if one is willing to measure such dimensions as sensitivity, understanding, and vision, then poetry promises a survival potential which technology can neither duplicate nor parallel.

It would be equally ridiculous to suggest that poetry is as easy as prose for young children to read and to understand. Nothing could be further from the truth. The hazards of figurative language, inverted sentences, extreme compression, and a strange, new format are all too real. Poems for young children need to be chosen with special care and, without exception, they should be read aloud *to* the child.

Listening to fine poetry read effectively by someone who loves it is a comfortable, almost familiar experience for the young child; not strange at all. Little children themselves tend to speak in cadenced prose that suggests the movement and rhythm of poetry. Moreover, since they still find pleasure in experimenting with speech sounds and rhythms at this stage of language development, young children usually enjoy and respond enthusiastically to these facets of poetry, even when the poet's intended meaning escapes them completely.

Because much of the early enjoyment of poetry is in *the sound of poetry,* young boys and girls should not only hear poetry frequently, but they should also be encouraged to participate in it by saying along with the parent or teacher those parts of a poem which appeal to them the most. At first these will undoubtedly be those strongly rhythmical and repetitive lines such as one finds in the nursery rhymes. Gradually, as children become more familiar with true poetry, they will want to expand their participation in it. Getting the "vocal feel" of poetry will enhance the child's enjoyment of many poems and in this and other ways help to ensure growth in appreciation.

Although the appeal of sound is probably stronger than that of meaning in the case of younger children, that is not to say that the content of poetry we give them is unimportant. The fun of seeing the ordinary through the eyes of the poet who recreates his own experiences can be as delightful to the child as it is to the adult. Anyone who really knows children, especially young children, is aware of the frustrations they often suffer as the result of a vocabulary too limited to express their feelings. What a relief it must be to a child to hear an expression of the pain, the beauty, the love he has felt but could not put into words. How comforting it must be to know that he is not alone in his feeling — that someone else has felt that way, too.

Give poetry to young children? Of course. Perhaps they need it more than anyone else. In any event, presenting it early and skillfully will help these youngsters grow naturally into the kind of persons who enjoy poetry and who seek its unique gifts for themselves. And it is also possible that the habit of sharing poetry is more productive of creative attempts when exposure to poetic expression precedes that self-consciousness which comes so soon in our culture.

Selecting Poetry for Children

Two guiding principles should be uppermost in the minds of adults who would choose for children poetry which has both an immediate and a lasting appeal: first, it must be excellent poetry; and second, it must be well within the range of children's appreciation. While some would place enjoyment before quality, selection should not be limited to what children obviously like. Boys and girls know what they like, but they are not aware of the pleasure to be gained from certain poems until the grown-up makes the best available to them. The appreciation of poetry is cumulative. Each experience should prepare children for a deeper appreciation of good literature by the way it stimulates their imagination and contributes to their wisdom.

There is no simple, sure test for distinguishing between excellence and mediocrity in children's poetry. There are, however, certain recognizable qualities or characteristics which appear to be associated with those poems for children which merit the label of authentic poetry. The durable poems of childhood are those which sharpen and enrich the child's perceptions of the familiar and the strange: help him to "see" his two worlds — the one outside and the one inside — in new and exciting ways. One senses even before analysis reveals it that such poems accomplish their special magic through a near perfect synthesis of subject matter and sound . . . content and composition. If it is good poetry, then the words and rhythms are those which serve best and are most appropriate for the poet's purpose. We respond to the expressive composition of a fine poem even though we may not realize the contribution it makes to meaning and mood. And so do children.

As the grown-up becomes more and more aware of those subtle relationships which exist among the elements of all true poetry, his own enjoyment and appreciation of poetry will be enhanced. Furthermore, he will become increasingly skillful in recognizing the poetic quality in the selections he chooses for children. He should remember, however, that perfection in poetry is much like our attempt to approximate absolute zero. To date we have only come close. The designation "best" is only a relative term. The goodness of fit between rhythm and words on the one hand and intended meaning on the other is always a matter of degree. If mere impression is to be transformed into good judgment, we must learn to recognize quality, or the lack of it, in each of the components of poetry as well as in their integration. Thus, it would seem wise at this point to examine at least briefly each of those elements which contribute to the total effect or impact a poem.

Any discussion of the basic elements of good poetry for children must begin with some reference to the natural beat or rhythm of the words and lines. One of the most obvious characteristics of much of the poetry for younger children is the presence of strong rhythmic patterns. Children enjoy marked rhythms and the anticipation of rhyme in poetry as they do in songs.

If it is good poetry, the movement will match the meaning — skipping nimbly through the nonsense verses; tiptoeing softly along the lovely lines of lyrics; sometimes marching, sometimes dancing, swinging, snapping, clicking, tapping according to the sound demands of content. If it is poor poetry, the rhymes will be forced, the rhythmic patterns monotonous and clumsy — ill fitted to the subject matter.

While the lilt and rhythms of poetry are of primary importance, there would be no poetry at all without words. The poet uses words to tell us something, perhaps a story or an impression of what he has seen or felt. He selects and uses words differently from the prose writer, however, who has a wealth of available words from which to choose. The poet is limited necessarily by such demands of his art as rhyme, meter, and that economy of statement which is the sign of excellence in poetic form. He must use a few words to say a great deal. The selection from this precious store of words must be made with immaculate precision. Words must suggest meanings and feelings as well as symbolize them. Furthermore, if they are to produce the desired effect, either singly or in juxtaposition by design, they must be rich in sensory appeal.

The use of rhymed words is not essential to the writing of fine poetry. It is, however, an obvious characteristic of many of the poems written for young children. The English language is rich in rhymes and the children's poets have discovered many different ways of producing these delightful sound effects. Most often the poet will strike one word against another at the ends of lines as in the simple nursery rhyme, "Jack and Jill/Went up the hill." At other times he may strike one word against another progressively along a line making each word vibrate musically. This effect was achieved by Laura E. Richards with the "jiggle joggle" of her little train refrain in "The Baby Goes to Boston."

> Loky moky poky stoky
> Smoky choky chee.

Or the poet may prefer to tease his young listener by playing games with words and rhymes in an obvious attempt to make him laugh. Hymes does this in his wonderful "Lunch."

> Pitter, patter
> Potter, putter
> Better, batter
> Peanut butter!

Hearing the music of poetry is not enough; one must also be able to sense what the poetry is trying to express, even if it's nonsense. Poetry, then, is an integration of music and content which really defies complete analysis. It can be distinguished from prose, however. If an author writes

At 6:30
Mark Roberts Llewellyn
Came in from his play
To have dinner with his family.

he is simply arranging prose in brief lines. If he writes, as Hilda Conkling did,

Little Mouse in gray velvet,
Have you had a cheese-breakfast?
There are no crumbs on your coat,
Did you use a napkin?
I wonder what you had to eat,
And who dresses you in gray velvet?

he is crystallizing an experience in a way that helps us realize that a poem means more than its words, regardless of the absence of rhyme and the presence of irregular rhythm and pattern. In other words, true poetry must stir the imagination and do it in a form which is not characteristic of prose.

Poems Used in This Anthology

From Mother Goose to T. S. Eliot and Marianne Moore is a "giant step," but it is one which children are not expected to accomplish within a short period of time. Moreover, nursery rhymes are stepping stones to quality poetry, and young children have reasons of their own for giving Mother Goose a permanent place in their hearts. Despite the variety in subject matter and style, all of the nursery rhymes appeal to the ear and the imagination. Whether children are chanting "Old Mother Hubbard/Went to the cupboard,/To get her poor dog a bone;" or listening to the lyrical

I had a little nut tree
Nothing would it bear
But a silver nutmeg
And a golden pear;

the rhymes appeal to the ear because they are truly musical. Frequently, however, the most popular ones with preschoolers are the rhyming jingles rather than those with lyrical qualities. Small children are attracted by alliterative lines of nonsense, just as they are intrigued by bright, clear colors, sparkling jewelry, and moving objects — "Hickory, dickory, dock;" "Hey diddle diddle!" "Pease porridge hot;" "Baa, baa, black sheep;" "Ring-around-a-rosy;" and others. Similarly, many rhymes almost sing themselves:

Mistress Mary, quite contrary,
How does your garden grow?
With silver bells, and cockleshells,
And pretty maids all in a row.

xix

And their music which is more in the manner of a folk tune than a polished concerto appeals to the child's enjoyment of rhythmical movement. Indeed, children often begin to wave their arms and to tap their feet as a natural accompaniment to these sprightly verses.

Aside from their musical qualities, nursery rhymes also appeal through their subject matter. Young children meet countless individuals through their delightful association with Mother Goose — individuals who have done something so distinctly unique that it will be forever identified with them: Little Miss Muffet will continue to be frightened by a spider, and Old King Cole will always call for his fiddlers three. An acquaintance with Mother Goose helps children develop a sense of rhythm, provokes mirth and laughter, stimulates the imagination, and provides an important transition to narrative and lyrical poetry.

Nursery rhymes first heard in childhood represent the initial exposure of most English-speaking children to poetically intended language. The sing-song rhythms and happy lines of these memorable little pieces often remain with us throughout life. At odd moments they come popping to the surface of memory, released by some chance cue. At other times they bob into awareness, tantalizingly familiar, yet just short of total recall. Among the richest treasures of childhood, these small verses may not be considered strictly as poems "to grow on," but they do provide a valid and delightful foundation on which to build. It seemed appropriate, therefore, to begin this anthology with a representative collection of these wonderful little rhymes and riddles.

The remaining sections of the book contain a rich variety of poems carefully selected for young listeners and arranged in thematic groupings for the convenience of teachers and parents. The beloved children's poets are well represented, but some of the works of other poets are also included. For in the final analysis, poetry for children is poetry which appeals to children whether it was intended for them or not.

It is possible that no one anthology will ever contain within its covers all of the poems, and only those poems, which the critics could agree are the finest coin of this golden realm. Few if any would ever be able to agree completely on either the hierarchy of merit or the cut-off point of worthwhileness for a particular developmental level. Most would agree, however, that children grow in appreciation of fine poetry as they are exposed to it.

It is true, as many have pointed out, that only the best efforts of the poet are good enough for children. This does not mean that the child is ready for all of the poet's best efforts. We must begin where the child is — where recognition is possible and sudden discovery comes easily. Thus, some of the poems in this collection are the simple, durable poems of childhood, the ones a child quickly makes his own for life. They can sensitize a child to poetry in a way that is non-reversible. This is their power and much of their merit.

But a child also needs poetry to extend and enrich experience. For this reason, many of the poems which appear in this anthology have been included because they afford immediate satisfaction *at some valid level of appreciation* while holding forth the promise of deeper and deeper enjoyment. Such poems are the building blocks of aesthetic development.

It will be noticed, for example, that a number of Japanese *haiku* have been selected for inclusion. This is a poetic form which contains seventeen syllables, usually divided into three lines of five, seven, and five. Generally, two lightly sketched pictures are compared or contrasted against a suggested seasonal background. Deceptively simply in form and language, these tiny jewel-like poems have subtle and often complex depths. More than most poems, they demand a creative act on the part of the reader or listener.

Delight in *haiku* is always a function of one's perceptiveness and the nature and memories of one's experience. Thus, pleasure can be derived from these carefully chosen *haiku* at many different levels. At first, the child's enjoyment may be simply literal or perhaps at the level of specific imagery. Involvement with nuance and symbolism is yet to come; and when he is ready for it, delight in first sensing and then coming to know the perfect integration of structure and meaning which is the essence of *haiku*.

How the Poems are Arranged

The poems in this book have been arbitrarily assigned to one of eleven broad categories of content. Each of these groupings has been subdivided and arranged in what appeared to the anthologists to be a logical order. In general, and wherever possible, the order of difficulty is progressive within each specific subdivision. The broad category "From Day to Day" provides a good example of the type of arrangement employed. The ordering in this case is chronological, beginning with bedtime. All of the poems about bedtime or those which are strongly associated with this particular time of day and event are grouped together with the less demanding poems appearing first. And so on around the clock. If the teacher or parent using this book will browse through it, he will discover rather quickly the specific arrangement used for each of the other ten categories.

Sharing Poetry with Children

Children's enjoyment of poetry is dependent upon the judicious selection of poems and upon interesting methods of presentation. The poems chosen for children must be suited to their experiences, their interests, and their general maturational levels. Not only must poetry be appropriate for children, but it must also appeal to the adults whose function it is to expose them to *the sound of poetry*.

Gaining Confidence in Reading Poetry Aloud. Many parents and teachers quail at the mere thought of reading poetry aloud to children. Certainly it is a skill which must be learned and one which demands practice. Unlike other forms of practice, it need not be tedious; in fact, once introduced to this special delight, grown-ups often find that their own appreciation of poetry seems to increase.

Before the adult is ready to present poetry orally, he should listen to fine poetry read superbly. This is not so difficult as it may appear at first. Many excellent recordings are now available and their number is increasing annually. Quite a few of our most gifted poets have been recorded reading their own poems. The authors of some of the world's most appealing poetry, of course, are either unknown or no longer living. It is our good fortune that several outstanding personalities of the theatre have recorded their personal interpretations of some of these poems for us.

Listening repeatedly to several of these recordings will give the novice a "feel" for the sound of poetry when it is well read. Recordings such as the following may be sampled for listening practice: *Robert Frost Reads His Poetry* (Caedmon TC 1060) 1957; Carl Sandburg reading *Carl Sandburg's Poems for Children* (Caedmon TC 1124) 1961; Dylan Thomas' *A Child's Christmas in Wales* (Caedmon TC-1002-B) 1958; Beatrice Lillie, Cyril Ritchard, and Stanley Holloway's *The Nonsense Verse of Carroll and Lear* (Caedmon TC 1078) 1957; and Julie Andrews and Martyn Green's *Tell It Again* (Angel Records 65041).

Times for Poetry. If children are to grow in their appreciation of poetry, its presentation must not be left to chance and odd moments. Time must be provided frequently within the children's schedule so that the development of appreciation can be regularly nourished and evaluated. But regularity does not mean every Tuesday at two o'clock. It implies rather the responsibility for reserving a special time for poetry which can be changed but never overlooked nor squeezed out of existence.

Poetry is such, however, that it cannot and should not be confined to a special time, no matter how flexible the scheduling. There are "teachable moments" for poetic appreciation, too, and when they emerge they should be gently caught and held quietly. Sometimes beauty experienced defies expression — but just the right poem shared with children at that moment may prove to be the most satisfying medium for suggesting the feeling that they are experiencing.

At other times, the imagery or sensory impact of a poem which the grown-up wishes to introduce to children may be conveyed best by a chance event. The first real flakes of snow in winter may trigger the mental image and emotional response needed to appreciate Haskin's "No sky at all;/no earth at all — and still/the snowflakes fall. . . ." Some poems need more than a visual accompaniment. A full-scale sensory illustration is demanded for anything more than a shallow appreciation of Christina Rossetti's lovely "Who Has Seen the Wind?" The thematic title of the poem mockingly chides the artist who would attempt to illustrate it with line and color alone. Here, all the stops must be pulled out; the children must experience the wind itself as well as its visual effects.

When there are sparks in the air or when a change of pace or lightness is called for to offset some heavier feelings, choose a humorous poem and take time to share it with the children. There are moments when the ridiculous should be prescribed, when laughter can be beckoned by such nimble non-sense as John Ciardi's gay spoof, "The Reason for the Pelican," or one or more of Edward Lear's hilarious verses. Poetry can help to clear the air, lift the spirits, or make us interested again.

The teacher or parent who realizes the importance of taking advantage of special occasions or children's moods to introduce poetry should have an ample supply of poems within easy reach. He may, in fact, wish to build a personal collection. For example, there might be a few carefully selected rain poems for the day when a long period of drought has ended with gentle, welcome rain drops. Or if John announces that he is going to the dentist, the teacher will want to bring forth Rose Fyleman's "I'd like to be a dentist with a plate upon the door/And a little bubbling fountain in the middle of the floor"; and if Mary has ridden on a donkey over the weekend, Walter de la Mare's "Nicholas Nye" is plucked from the file to share with the group. Even the new teacher who has his own card file and one or two good anthologies can capitalize upon these special moments when the atmosphere and mood are just right for poetry.

Preparing Poems for Listening. Be prepared to read aloud the poem you wish to share with children. Find a poem that appeals to you. Read it silently, first. Then try it aloud several times. If a tape recorder is available, it would be beneficial to tape the poem and listen to it. You may want to listen to the poem several times in order to appraise those areas where changes might be needed.

When you practice-read a poem, try to identify with the thought, the mood, and the spirit which the words must convey. Speak clearly but avoid overly precise diction and dramatic exaggeration. As you read, feel for the music — the flow of rhythmical language — that was in the poet's mind. Say the words naturally in this same cadenced pattern. If you hear yourself reading in a mechanical or sing-song fashion, check yourself. Perhaps you are coming down hard on accented syllables — emphasizing the metric beat instead of letting your voice flow along with the natural rhythm of speech.

Perhaps you are allowing your voice to drop at the end of a line, instead of pausing between ideas and letting the voice rise and fall naturally with the thought. Or it could be that you are stressing the rhyming words too much. The next time you read it, try telling your poem instead of reciting it.

Grown-ups who wish to share poetry with children need to have a growing repertoire of poems they are prepared to read aloud. Some poems are easy to read, and preparation will require very little time; others demand considerable study and practice. In any event, preparing poems for oral presentation should be an ongoing procedure, and it is one from which the adult will derive increasing pleasure as reading skill improves.

Inviting Receptivity to Poetry. Not every child will respond to poetry at first, but frequent short exposures to the sound of worthwhile poems under the best possible conditions will encourage receptivity and the growth of appreciation. Children can be brought to poetry and poetry should be brought to children. It is the responsibility of parents and teachers to help young children discover the special delight that is poetry, so that for them it can become "indigenous" early.

For children learning to experience poetry, poetry reading time should be brief, but unhurried. It is often wise to concentrate on a single poem, or perhaps two somewhat different ones if they have a similar theme and are appropriate in terms of the current interest of the group. Make room also from time to time for old favorites. Such requests are clues to the growth of appreciation. Variety is important, too. Introduce children to many different forms — story-telling poems, nonsense rhymes, unrhymed verse, lyrics, folk poems, and those poems intended for singing. Remember to end each poetry reading when interest begins to slip away; preferably when attention is at its apex — that point at which feelings of satisfaction and "wanting more" blend.

Children must be in the mood for poetry or they will ignore it. Various factors contribute to a good listening climate, but none is more vital perhaps than physical comfort. Poetry time saved for the end of the day may appear to be a special treat, but tired muscles may not be able to remain quiet. If the children seem restless, a short recess may restore their equilibrium. On the other hand, if they are too stirred up after physical activity, a short quiet time before attempting to present poetry is needed. Encourage children to relax in their seats, and be permissive about the position they prefer. Also try reading poetry early in the morning, when most children are bright-eyed-alert and receptive.

At times, the grown-up may wish to provide something very special and beautiful for children to focus upon while listening. A single, perfect rose, a lovely painting, an exquisite piece of china, silver, or rich textured brocade, a miniature and beautifully fragile snowstorm in a clear crystal paper weight, possibly a wonderfully colored gem or a bit of impressionistic music — such aesthetic objects and experiences will often help to invite and sustain a listening and receptive mood.

Poetry's magic spell, however, probably depends more upon the quality of the reading than upon anything else. The importance of presenting a poem successfully the first time cannot be overemphasized. Swift, superficial, and irrevocable — the judgment "I don't like that!" can ruin a particular poem and sometimes a whole poetry session, even for those who would otherwise have enjoyed it. As in other arts, we must encourage children to withhold unqualified pronouncements and to take time to absorb, reflect upon, and hear again the poem in question, thereby developing reasons for their judgment.

Discussing Poems. Too much discussion or analysis of poetry can spoil it for the novice listener. A few introductory remarks may be in order to appraise experiential backgrounds and to ensure at least a modicum of common knowledge with which to approach a particular poem. A key word, reference, or usage may need some clarification. An interesting but brief note about the poet or the poem may enhance anticipation in some instances. A poem that requires much explanation, however, is too difficult for young children and should not be used.

Ideally, it is well to let children initiate discussion after a poem has been presented. If no responses are made during the brief moments following the reading, read the poem again. Children may then have some comments to make, or a question to ask. From their reactions, the parent or teacher can decide what discussion will be helpful.

Discussion may be originated by the adult, of course, but one should avoid asking the stereotyped question "Did you like this poem?" for often this will evoke the very unqualified remark that should be discouraged. Instead, questions should be asked which will lead children to think more deeply: "Did you hear an interesting word picture? Have you ever felt the way the poet may have felt in this poem? Was part of the poem said in a way that you might like to remember? Why?" Such questions often lead to a request to reread the poem. When this is done, the second reading may produce more meaningful associations because children are listening for specific purposes. Always be certain, however, that attention is focused upon the poem itself, not upon the subject matter. Resist the temptation to allow a poem to set off a chain reaction of irrelevant discussions. Too many poems have been buried under an avalanche of flying hands and children's voices eager to relate their personal experiences.

What About Memorization? The memorization of poetry should be voluntary and for pleasure; not as a chore or requirement. As Robert Frost has commented, "Pretty things well said — It's nice to have them in your head." Young children enjoy participating in the repetitive refrains of nursery rhymes and folk poems. For example, in the poem, "Poor Old Lady," they'll love saying along with the reader the words, "I don't know why she swallowed the fly; Poor old lady, I think she'll die." This is a thoroughly enjoyable and natural way for small children to "take over" such poems as these for themselves.

When children learn to love a poem and hear it read aloud many times by someone who also enjoys it, they just naturally want to make it their own, and usually do.

Someone once said, "To be young without poetry is like being indoors in spring." The grown-up who introduces children to the sound of poetry opens doors to loveliness that lasts.

Mary C. Austin

Queenie B. Mills

Contents

Rhymes
And
Riddles

MOTHER GOOSE

Unknown

Old Mother Goose, when
She wanted to wander,
Would ride through the air
On a very fine gander.

SWEEPING THE SKY

Unknown

There was an old woman tossed up in a basket,
Ninety times as high as the moon;
And where she was going, I couldn't but ask it
For in her hand she carried a broom.

"Old woman, old woman, old woman," quoth I,
"Whither, O whither, O whither so high?"
"To sweep the cob-webs off the sky!"
"Shall I go with you?" "Aye, by-and-by."

THE CROOKED SIXPENCE

Mother Goose

There was a crooked man, and he walked a crooked mile,
He found a crooked sixpence beside a crooked stile;
He bought a crooked cat, which caught a crooked mouse,
And they all lived together in a little crooked house.

OLD MOTHER HUBBARD

Mother Goose

Old Mother Hubbard
Went to the cupboard,
To get her poor dog a bone;
But when she got there,
The cupboard was bare,
And so the poor dog had none.

PETER, PETER, PUMPKIN-EATER

Mother Goose

Peter, Peter, pumpkin-eater,
Had a wife and couldn't keep her;
He put her in a pumpkin shell,
And there he kept her very well.

THE GRAND OLD DUKE OF YORK

Mother Goose

The grand Old Duke of York
He had ten thousand men,
He marched them up a very high hill
And he marched them down again.
And when he was up he was up
And when he was down he was down
And when he was only halfway up
He was neither up nor down.

OLD KING COLE

Mother Goose

Old King Cole
Was a merry old soul,
And a merry old soul was he;
He called for his pipe,
He called for his bowl,
And he called for his fiddlers three.

Every fiddler, he had a fine fiddle
And a very fine fiddle had he;
Then twee, tweedle-dee,
Tweedle-dee went the fiddlers.

Oh, there's none so rare
As can compare
With King Cole and his fiddlers three!

A WEEK OF BIRTHDAYS

Mother Goose

Monday's child is fair of face,
Tuesday's child is full of grace,
Wednesday's child is full of woe,
Thursday's child has far to go,
Friday's child is loving and giving,
Saturday's child works hard for its living,
But the child that's born on the Sabbath day
Is bonny and blithe, and good and gay.

BYE, BABY BUNTING

Mother Goose

Bye, baby bunting,
Father's gone a-hunting,
Mother's gone a-milking,
Sister's gone a-silking,
And brother's gone to buy a skin
To wrap the baby bunting in.

5

SEE-SAW, MARGERY DAW

Mother Goose

See-saw, Margery Daw,
And Jack shall have a new master;
He shall have but a penny a day,
Because he can't work any faster.

LITTLE BOY BLUE

Mother Goose

Little boy blue, come blow your horn;
The sheep's in the meadow, the cow's in the corn.
Where's the little boy that looks after the sheep?
He's under the haystack, fast asleep.

LITTLE JACK HORNER

Mother Goose

Little Jack Horner
Sat in a corner
Eating his Christmas pie;
He put in his thumb,
And pulled out a plum,
And said, "What a good boy am I!"

JACK BE NIMBLE

Mother Goose

> Jack be nimble,
> Jack be quick,
> And Jack jump over
> The candlestick.

JACK AND JILL

Mother Goose

> Jack and Jill
> Went up the hill,
> To fetch a pail of water;
> Jack fell down,
> And broke his crown,
> And Jill came tumbling after.

MISTRESS MARY

Mother Goose

> Mistress Mary, quite contrary,
> How does your garden grow?
> With silver bells, and cockleshells,
> And pretty maids all in a row.

WEE WILLIE WINKIE

Mother Goose

Wee Willie Winkie
  Runs through the town,
Upstairs and downstairs,
  In his nightgown;
Rapping at the window,
  Crying through the lock,
"Are the children in their beds?
  For now it's eight o'clock."

CURLY LOCKS

Mother Goose

Curly locks! Curly locks!
  Wilt thou be mine?
Thou shalt not wash dishes
  Nor yet feed the swine.
But sit on a cushion
  And sew a fine seam,
And feed upon strawberries
  Sugar and cream.

LITTLE MISS MUFFET

Mother Goose

Little Miss Muffet
Sat on a tuffet,
Eating of curds and whey;
There came a great spider,
And sat down beside her,
And frightened Miss Muffet away.

HIPPETY HOP TO THE BARBER SHOP

Mother Goose

Hippety hop to the barber shop,
To get a stick of candy,
One for you and one for me,
And one for Sister Mandy.

SIMPLE SIMON

Mother Goose

Simple Simon met a pieman,
Going to the fair;
Says Simple Simon to the pieman,
"Let me taste your ware."

9

Says the pieman unto Simon,
  "Show me first your penny."
Says Simple Simon to the pieman,
  "Indeed, I have not any."

MIX A PANCAKE

Christina Rossetti

Mix a pancake,
Stir a pancake,
  Pop it in the pan;
Fry the pancake,
Toss the pancake, —
  Catch it if you can.

PEASE PORRIDGE HOT

Mother Goose

Pease porridge hot,
Pease porridge cold,
Pease porridge in the pot,
Nine days old.
Some like it hot,
Some like it cold,
Some like it in the pot,
Nine days old.

HANDY SPANDY

Mother Goose

Handy Spandy, Jack-a-dandy,
Loved plum cake and sugar candy;
He bought some at a grocer's shop,
And out he came, hop, hop, hop.

BLOW, WIND, BLOW

Mother Goose

Blow, wind, blow!
And go, mill, go!
That the miller may grind his corn;
That the baker may take it,
And into bread make it
And bring us a loaf in the morn.

HOT-CROSS BUNS

Mother Goose

Hot-cross buns!
Hot-cross buns!
One a penny, two a penny,
Hot-cross buns!

Hot-cross buns!
Hot-cross buns!
If you have no daughters,
Give them to your sons.

THE HOUSE THAT JACK BUILT

Unknown

This is the house that Jack built.

This is the malt
That lay in the house that Jack built.

This is the rat,
That ate the malt
That lay in the house that Jack built.

This is the cat,
That killed the rat,
That ate the malt
That lay in the house that Jack built.

This is the dog,
That worried the cat,
That killed the rat,
That ate the malt
That lay in the house that Jack built.

HEY, DIDDLE, DIDDLE

Mother Goose

Hey, diddle, diddle!
The cat and the fiddle,
The cow jumped over the moon;
The little dog laughed
To see such sport,
And the dish ran away with the spoon.

LADYBIRD, LADYBIRD

Mother Goose

Ladybird, Ladybird, fly away home,
Your house is on fire, your children all gone,
All but one, and her name is Ann
And she crept under a pudding-pan.

LITTLE BO-PEEP

Mother Goose

Little Bo-Peep has lost her sheep,
And can't tell where to find them;
Leave them alone, and they'll come home,
And bring their tails behind them.

DING, DONG, BELL

Mother Goose

Ding, Dong, bell,
Pussy's in the well!
Who put her in?
Little Tommy Green.
Who pulled her out?
Little Johnny Stout.
What a naughty boy was that,
To try to drown poor pussy cat,
Who never did him any harm,
But killed the mice in his father's barn.

MARY'S LAMB

Sarah Josepha Hale

Mary had a little lamb,
　Its fleece was white as snow;
And everywhere that Mary went
　The lamb was sure to go.

He followed her to school one day;
　That was against the rule;
It made the children laugh and play
　To see a lamb at school.

14

And so the teacher turned him out,
    But still he lingered near,
And waited patiently about
    Till Mary did appear.

"What makes the lamb love Mary so?"
    The eager children cry.
"Oh, Mary loves the lamb, you know,"
    The teacher did reply.

RIDE A COCKHORSE

Mother Goose

Ride a cockhorse to Banbury Cross,
To see a fine lady upon a white horse.
    With rings on her fingers,
    And bells on her toes,
She shall have music wherever she goes.

PUSSYCAT, PUSSYCAT

Mother Goose

Pussycat, pussycat, where have you been?
I've been to London to visit the Queen.
Pussycat, pussycat, what did you there?
I frightened a little mouse under the chair.

SING A SONG OF SIXPENCE

Mother Goose

Sing a song of sixpence,
  A pocket full of rye,
Four and twenty blackbirds
  Baked in a pie.
When the pie was opened,
  The birds began to sing.
Wasn't that a dainty dish
  To set before the King?

The King was in his counting house
  Counting out his money;
The Queen was in her parlor,
  Eating bread and honey;
The maid was in the garden,
  Hanging out the clothes,
Down came a blackbird
  And snapped off her nose.

HIGGLEDY, PIGGLEDY

Mother Goose

Higgledy, piggledy, my black hen,
She lays eggs for gentlemen;

16

Sometimes nine, and sometimes ten,
Higgledy, piggledy, my black hen.

HICKORY, DICKORY, DOCK

Mother Goose

Hickory, dickory, dock,
The mouse ran up the clock.
The clock struck one,
The mouse ran down;
Hickory, dickory, dock.

BAA, BAA, BLACK SHEEP

Mother Goose

Baa, baa, black sheep,
    Have you any wool?
Yes, sir, yes, sir,
    Three bags full;

One for my master,
    One for my dame,
And one for the little boy
    Who lives down the lane.

17

THIS LITTLE PIG WENT TO MARKET

Mother Goose

This little pig went to market;
This little pig stayed at home;
This little pig had roast beef;
This little pig had none;
This little pig said, "Wee, wee!
I can't find my way home."

TO MARKET, TO MARKET

Mother Goose

To market, to market, to buy a fat pig,
Home again, home again, jiggety jig.

To market, to market, to buy a fat hog,
Home again, home again, jiggety jog.

To market, to market, to buy a plum bun,
Home again, home again, market is done.

I HAD A LITTLE PONY

Mother Goose

I had a little pony,
　　His name was Dapple-gray,
I lent him to a lady,
　　To ride a mile away;
She whipped him, she slashed him,
　　She rode him through the mire;
I would not lend my pony now
　　For all the lady's hire.

I SAW A SHIP A-SAILING

Mother Goose

I saw a ship a-sailing,
A-sailing on the sea;
And, oh, it was all laden
With pretty things for thee.
There were comfits in the cabin,
And apples in the hold;
The sails were made of satin,
The masts were made of gold.
The four-and-twenty sailors
That stood between the decks,
Were four-and-twenty white mice,
With chains about their necks.

The Captain was a duck, a duck,
With a jacket on his back;
And when the ship began to move
The Captain said, "Quack, quack."

STAR LIGHT, STAR BRIGHT

American Mother Goose

Star light, star bright,
First star I see tonight,
I wish I may, I wish I might,
Have the wish I wish tonight.

RING-AROUND-A-ROSY

Mother Goose

Ring-around-a-rosy
A pocket full of posies;
One, two, three,
And we all fall down!

ONE, TWO, BUCKLE MY SHOE

Mother Goose

One, two,
Buckle my shoe;

Three, four,
Knock at the door;

Five, six,
Pick up sticks;

Seven, eight,
Lay them straight;

Nine, ten,
A good fat hen.

LOOBY LOO

Unknown

Here we dance Looby Loo,
Here we dance Looby Light,
Here we dance Looby Loo,
Dance with all your might.

Put your right hand in — and your right hand out,
Shake yourself a little, and turn yourself about.

THREE LITTLE KITTENS

Eliza Cook

Three little kittens lost their mittens,
And they began to cry,
"Oh, Mother dear,
We sadly fear
That we have lost our mittens."

"Lost your mittens!
You naughty kittens!
Then you shall have no pie."
"Mee-ow, mee-ow, mee-ow."
"No, you shall have no pie,"
"Mee-ow, mee-ow, mee-ow."

Three little kittens found their mittens,
And they began to cry,
"Oh, mother dear,
See here, see here
See, we have found our mittens."

"What, found your mittens,
   You little kittens,
Then you may have some pie."
   "Purr-r, purr-r, purr-r."
"Oh, let us have the pie."
   "Purr-r, purr-r, purr-r."

The three little kittens put on their mittens,
   And soon ate up the pie.
      "Oh, mother dear,
         We greatly fear
That we have soiled our mittens."

      "Soiled your mittens!
         You naughty kittens!"
Then they began to sigh,
      "Mee-ow, mee-ow, mee-ow."
Then they began to sigh,
      "Mee-ow, mee-ow, mee-ow."

The three little kittens washed their mittens,
   And hung them out to dry.
      "Oh, mother dear,
         Look here, look here!
See, we have washed our mittens."

      "Washed your mittens!
      Oh, you're good kittens.
      But I smell a rat close by.
      Hush, hush! Mee-ow, mee-ow."
      "We smell a rat near by."
      "Mee-ow, mee-ow, mee-ow."

THE NUT TREE

Mother Goose

I had a little nut tree,
   Nothing would it bear,
But a silver nutmeg
   And a golden pear;
The King of Spain's daughter
   Came to visit me,
And all for the sake
   Of my little nut tree.
I skipped over water,
   I danced over sea,
And all the birds in the air
   Couldn't catch me.

RIDDLES

Mother Goose

Lives in winter,
   Dies in summer,
And grows with its roots upward!
                     (An Icicle)

Mother Goose

Higher than a house,
Higher than a tree,
Oh! whatever can that be?
(A Star)

Mother Goose

Little Nancy Etticoat,
In a white petticoat,
And a red nose.
The longer she stands,
The shorter she grows.
(A Candle)

Mother Goose

Thirty white horses
On a red hill;
Now they tramp,
Now they champ,
Now they stand still.
(The Teeth and Gums)

Mother Goose

As I was going to St. Ives,
I met a man with seven wives;
Each wife had seven sacks,
Each sack had seven cats,
Each cat had seven kits.
Kits, cats, sacks, and wives,
How many were going to St. Ives?
                                    (One)

Mother Goose

Old Mother Twitchet had but one eye,
And a long tail that she let fly;
And every time she went through a gap,
She left a bit of her tail in a trap.
                    (A Needle and Thread)

Unknown

A shoemaker makes shoes without leather,
With all four elements put together,
Fire, Water, Earth, Air,
And every customer takes two pair.
                        (A Blacksmith)

Mother Goose

A hill full, a hole full,
You cannot catch a bowl full.
(Mist or smoke)

RHYMING RIDDLES

Mary Austin

I come more softly than a bird,
And lovely as a flower;
I sometimes last from year to year
And sometimes but an hour.

I stop the swiftest railroad train
Or break the stoutest tree.
And yet I am afraid of fire
And children play with me.
(Snow)

Mary Austin

I have no wings, but yet I fly,
I'm slender as a snake and straight as rain,
Who takes me in must die,
Who lets me quickly go will surest gain.
(Arrow)

Animals
All

THE ANIMAL FAIR

Unknown

I went to the animal fair,
The birds and beasts were there.
The big baboon, by the light of the moon,
Was combing his auburn hair.
The monkey, he got drunk,
And sat on the elephant's trunk.
The elephant sneezed and fell on his knees,
And what became of the monk, the monk?

SONG FOR A CHILD

Helen B. Davis

My kitty has a little song
She hums inside of her;
She curls up by the kitchen fire
And then begins to purr.

It sounds just like she's winding up
A tiny clock she keeps
Inside her beautiful fur coat
To wake her, when she sleeps.

CATS

Marchette Chute

A baby cat is soft and sweet.
It tangles in around your feet.

But when a cat is fully grown,
It often likes to be alone.

CAT

Mary Britton Miller

The black cat yawns,
Opens her jaws,
Stretches her legs,
And shows her claws.

Then she gets up
And stands on four
Long stiff legs
And yawns some more.

She shows her sharp teeth,
She stretches her lip,
Her slice of a tongue
Turns up at the tip.

Lifting herself
On her delicate toes,
She arches her back
As high as it goes.

She lets herself down
With particular care,
And pads away
With her tail in the air.

I LOVE LITTLE PUSSY

Jane Taylor

I love little Pussy
    Her coat is so warm;
And if I don't hurt her,
    She'll do me no harm.

So I'll not pull her tail,
    Nor drive her away,
But Pussy and I
    Very gently will play.

She shall sit by my side,
    And I'll give her some food;
And she'll love me, because
    I am gentle and good.

I never will vex her,
    Nor make her displeased,
For Puss doesn't like
    To be worried or teased.

THE MYSTERIOUS CAT

Vachel Lindsay

I saw a proud, mysterious cat,
I saw a proud, mysterious cat
Too proud to catch a mouse or rat —
Mew, mew, mew.

But catnip she would eat, and purr,
But catnip she would eat, and purr.
And goldfish she did much prefer —
Mew, mew, mew.

I saw a cat — 'twas but a dream,
I saw a cat — 'twas but a dream
Who scorned the slave that brought her cream —
Mew, mew, mew.

Unless the slave were dressed in style,
Unless the slave were dressed in style
And knelt before her all the while —
Mew, mew, mew.

Did you ever hear of a thing like that?
Did you ever hear of a thing like that?
Did you ever hear of a thing like that?
Oh, what a proud mysterious cat.
Oh, what a proud mysterious cat.
Oh, what a proud mysterious cat.
Mew . . . Mew . . . Mew.

CAT

Dorothy Baruch

My cat
Is quiet.
She moves without a sound.
Sometimes she stretches herself high and curving
On tiptoe.
Sometimes she crouches low
And creeping.

Sometimes she rubs herself against a chair,
And there
   With a *miew* and a *miew*
   And a purrr purrr purrr
   She curls up
   And goes to sleep.

My cat
Lives through a black hole

Under the house.
So one day I
Crawled in after her.
And it was dark
And I sat
And didn't know
Where to go.
And then —

Two yellow-white
Round little lights
Came moving . . . moving . . . toward me.
And there
With a *miew* and a *miew*
   And a purrr purrr purrr
My cat
Rubbed, soft, against me.

   And I knew
   The lights
   Were MY CAT'S EYES
   In the dark.

TIGER-CAT TIM

Edith Newlin Chase

Timothy Tim was a very small cat
Who looked like a tiger the size of a rat.

There were little black stripes running all over him,
With just enough white on his feet for a trim
On Tiger-cat Tim.

Timothy Tim had a little pink tongue
That was spoon, comb and washcloth all made into one.
He lapped up his milk, washed and combed all his fur,
And then he sat down in the sunshine to purr
Full little Tim.

Timothy Tim had a queer little way
Of always pretending at things in his play.
He caught pretend mice in the grass and the sand
And fought pretend cats when he played with your hand,
Fierce little Tim!

He drank all his milk, and he grew and he grew,
He ate all his meat and his vegetables too,
He grew very big and he grew very fat,
And now he's a lazy old, sleepy old cat,
Timothy Tim!

PUPPY

Aileen Fisher

> My puppy likes
> a hard old bone
> as if it were
> an ice-cream cone.

MY DOG

Marchette Chute

His nose is short and scrubby;
   His ears hang rather low;
And he always brings the stick back,
   No matter how far you throw.

He gets spanked rather often
   For things he shouldn't do,
Like lying-on-beds, and barking,
   And eating up shoes when they're new.

He always wants to be going
   Where he isn't supposed to go.
He tracks up the house when it's snowing,
   Oh, puppy, I love you so.

THE HAIRY DOG

Herbert Asquith

My dog's so furry I've not seen
His face for years and years:
His eyes are buried out of sight,
I only guess his ears.

37

When people ask me for his breed,
I do not know or care:
He has the beauty of them all
Hidden beneath his hair.

MY AIREDALE DOG

W. L. Mason

I have a funny Airedale dog,
   He's just about my size,
With such a serious-looking face,
   And eyes that seem so wise.

He looks as if he'd like to laugh,
   But yet his long, straight muzzle
Gives him a kind of solemn look —
   He surely is a puzzle.

And he is just as full of tricks
   As any dog could be,
And we have mighty jolly times
   Because he plays with me,

And never tries to bite or snap;
   He doesn't even whine —
And that is why my Airedale dog
   Is such a friend of mine.

MY DOG

Tom Robinson

My dog listens when I talk.
He goes with me for a walk.
When I sleep, he's sleepy too.
He does everything I do.
He has eyes that always show
He knows everything I know.
I never do a thing but he
Thinks it is all right for me.
When I speak, he always minds.
He shares with me the things he finds.
When other people say I'm bad,
He hangs his head and looks so sad.
He cuddles up and laps my hand
And tells me he can understand.

PUPPY AND I

A. A. Milne

I met a man as I went walking;
We got talking,
Man and I.
"Where are you going to, Man?" I said

(I said to the Man as he went by).
"Down to the village, to get some bread.
Will you come with me?" "No, not I."

I met a Horse as I went walking;
We got talking,
Horse and I.
"Where are you going to, Horse, today?"
(I said to the Horse as he went by).
"Down to the village to get some hay.
Will you come with me?" "No, not I."

I met a Woman as I went walking;
We got talking,
Woman and I.
"Where are you going to, Woman, so early?"
(I said to the Woman as she went by).
"Down to the village to get some barley.
Will you come with me?" "No, not I."

I met some Rabbits as I went walking;
We got talking,
Rabbits and I.
"Where are you going in your brown fur coats?"
(I said to the Rabbits as they went by).
"Down to the village to get some oats.
Will you come with us?" "No, not I."

I met a Puppy as I went walking;
We got talking,

40

Puppy and I.
"Where are you going this nice fine day?"
(I said to the Puppy as he went by).
"Up in the hills to roll and play."
"I'll come with you, Puppy," said I.

VERY EARLY

Karla Kuskin

When I wake in the early mist
The sun has hardly shown
And everything is still asleep
And I'm awake alone.
The stars are faint and flickering.
The sun is new and shy.
And all the world sleeps quietly,
Except the sun and I.
And then beginning noises start,
The whrrs and huffs and hums,
The birds peep out to find a worm,
The mice squeak out for crumbs,
The calf moos out to find the cow,
And taste the morning air
And everything is wide awake
And running everywhere.
The dew has dried,
The fields are warm,
The day is loud and bright,
And I'm the one who woke the sun
And kissed the stars good night.

FAMILIAR FRIENDS

James S. Tippett

The horses, the pigs,
And the chickens,
The turkeys, the ducks
And the sheep!
I can see all my friends
From my window
As soon as I waken
From sleep.

The cat on the fence
Is out walking.
The geese have gone down
For a swim.
The pony comes trotting
Right up to the gate;
He knows I have candy
For him.

The cows in the pasture
Are switching
Their tails to keep off
The flies.
And the old mother dog
Has come out in the yard
With five pups to give me
A surprise.

THE COW

Robert Louis Stevenson

The friendly cow all red and white,
  I love with all my heart:
She gives me cream, with all her might,
  To eat with apple-tart.

She wanders lowing here and there,
  And yet she cannot stray,
All in the pleasant open air,
  The pleasant light of day;

And blown by all the winds that pass
  And wet with all the showers,
She walks among the meadow grass
  And eats the meadow flowers.

THE NEW BABY CALF

Edith Newlin Chase

Buttercup, the cow, had a new baby calf,
      a fine baby calf,
        a strong baby calf,

43

Not strong like his mother
But strong for a calf,
For *this* baby calf was so *new!*

Buttercup licked him with her strong warm tongue,
Buttercup washed him with her strong warm tongue,
Buttercup brushed him with her strong warm tongue,
    And the new baby calf *liked that!*

The new baby calf took a very little walk,
            a tiny little walk,
                a teeny little walk,

But his long legs wobbled
When he took a little walk,
    And the new baby calf fell down.

Buttercup told him with a low soft "Moo-oo!"
That he was doing very well for one so very new
And she talked very gently, as mother cows do,
    And the new baby calf *liked that!*

The new baby calf took another little walk,
            a little longer walk,
                a little stronger walk,
He walked around his mother and he found the place to drink.
    And the new baby calf liked *that!*

Buttercup told him with another low moo
That drinking milk from mother was a fine thing to do,

That she had lots of milk for him and for the farmer too,
    And the new baby calf liked *that!*

The new baby calf drank milk every day,
His legs grew so strong that he could run and play,
He learned to eat grass and then grain and hay,
    And the big baby calf grew fat!

CATTLE

Unknown

How cool the cattle seem!
They love to swish their tails and stand
Knee-deep within the stream.

THE PASTURE

Robert Frost

I'm going out to clean the pasture spring;
I'll only stop to rake the leaves away
(And wait to watch the water clear, I may):
I shan't be gone long. — You come too.

I'm going out to fetch the little calf
That's standing by the mother. It's so young
It totters when she licks it with her tongue.
I shan't be gone long. — You come too.

TROT ALONG, PONY

Marion Edey and Dorothy Grider

Trot along, pony.
Late in the day,
Down by the meadow
Is the loveliest way.

The apples are rosy
And ready to fall.
The branches hang over
By Grandfather's wall.

But the red sun is sinking
Away out of sight.
The chickens are settling
Themselves for the night.

Your stable is waiting
And supper will come.
So turn again, pony,
Turn again home.

WORK HORSES

Edith Newlin Chase

Big strong work horses working every day,
Big strong work horses pulling loads of hay,
Big strong work horses have no time to play,
   Work! — Work! — Work!
Big strong work horses with a wagon full,
Big strong work horses, pull! pull! pull!
   Pull! — Pull! — Pull!

  Big horse, strong horse,
  Pull the plow, pull the plow,
  Pull hard, work hard,
  Plow the garden, plow, plow!
  Big horse, tired horse,
  Stop and rest now.

Big strong work horses plowing up the ground,
Big strong work horses walking round and round,
Big strong work horses going home to lunch,
Eat oats, eating hay, munch! munch! munch!

THE MILKMAN'S HORSE

Unknown

On summer mornings when it's hot,
The milkman's horse can't even trot;
But pokes along like this —
Klip-klop, Klip-klop, Klip-klop.

But in the winter brisk,
He perks right up and wants to frisk;
And then he goes like this —
Klippity-klip, Klippity-klip, Klippity-klip.

THE HAPPY SHEEP

Wilfred Thorley

All through the night the happy sheep
Lie in the meadow grass asleep.

Their wool keeps out the frost and rain
Until the sun comes round again.

They have no buttons to undo,
Nor hair to brush like me and you.

And with the light they lift their heads
To find their breakfast on their beds,

Or rise and walk about and eat
The carpet underneath their feet.

I HELD A LAMB

Kim Worthington

One day when I went visiting,
A little lamb was there,
I picked it up and held it tight,
It didn't seem to care.

Its wool was soft and felt so warm —
Like sunlight on the sand,
And when I gently put it down
It licked me on the hand.

THE COCK AGAIN

Kikaku

The cock again
is fighting like a lion:
see his mane!

CHANTICLEER

John Farrar

High and proud on the barnyard fence
Walks rooster in the morning.
He shakes his comb, he shakes his tail
And gives his daily warning.

"Get up, you lazy boys and girls,
It's time you should be dressing!"
I wonder if he keeps a clock,
Or if he's only guessing.

THE HENS

Elizabeth Madox Roberts

The night was coming very fast;
It reached the gate as I ran past.

The pigeons had gone to the tower of the church
And all the hens were on their perch,

Up in the barn, and I thought I heard
A piece of a little purring word.

I stopped inside, waiting and staying,
To try to hear what the hens were saying.

They were asking something, that was plain,
Asking it over and over again.

One of them moved and turned around,
Her feathers made a ruffled sound,

A ruffled sound, like a bushful of birds,
And she said her little asking words.

She pushed her head close into her wing,
But nothing answered anything.

DUCKS' DITTY

Kenneth Grahame

All along the backwater,
Through the rushes tall,
Ducks are a-dabbling,
Up tails all!

Ducks' tails, drakes' tails,
Yellow feet a-quiver,

Yellow bills all out of sight
Busy in the river!

Slushy green undergrowth
Where the roach swim —
Here we keep our larder,
Cool and full and dim.

Everyone for what he likes!
We like to be
Heads down, tails up,
Dabbling free!

High in the blue above
Swifts whirl and call —
We are down a-dabbling
Up tails all!

DUCKS AT DAWN

James S. Tippett

"Quack! Quack!"
Said seven ducks at dawn
While night dew
Glimmered on the lawn.

"Quack! Quack!" they said.
"It's time to eat.
We'll go hunt mushrooms
For a treat."

And in the light
Of early dawn
I saw them chasing
On the lawn.

They sought their treat
With hungry quacks
And marked the dew
With criss-cross tracks.

They ate the mushrooms
One by one
And quacked to greet
The rising sun.

But in my bed
I settled back
And slept to tunes
Of "Quack! Quack! Quack!"

THE LITTLE DUCK

Jōsō

"I've just come from a place
    at the lake bottom!" — that is the look
    on the little duck's face.

REGENT'S PARK

Rose Fyleman

What makes the ducks in the pond, I wonder, go
Suddenly under?

Down they go in the neatest way;
You'd be surprised at the time they stay,
You stand on the bank and you wait and stare,
Trying to think what they do down there;
And, just as you're feeling anxious, then
Suddenly up they come again,
Ever so far from where you guessed,
Dry and tidy and self-possessed.

What is it makes the duck, I wonder, go
Suddenly under?

MICE

Rose Fyleman

I think mice
Are rather nice.

Their tails are long,
Their faces small,
They haven't any
Chins at all.
Their ears are pink,
Their teeth are white,
They run about
The house at night.
They nibble things
They shouldn't touch
And no one seems
To like them much.

But I think mice
Are nice.

THE HOUSE OF THE MOUSE

Lucy Sprague Mitchell

The house of the mouse
is a wee little house,
a green little house in the grass,
which big clumsy folk
may hunt and may poke
and still never see as they pass
this sweet little, neat little,
wee little, green little,
cuddle-down hide-away
house in the grass.

THE MOUSE

Elizabeth Coatsworth

I heard a mouse
Bitterly complaining
In a crack of moonlight
Aslant on the floor —

"Little I ask
And that little is not granted.
There are few crumbs
In this world any more.

56

"The bread-box is tin
And I cannot get in.

"The jam's in a jar
My teeth cannot mar.

"The cheese sits by itself
On the pantry shelf —

"All night I run
Searching and seeking,
All night I run
About on the floor.

"Moonlight is there
And a bare place for dancing,
But no little feast
Is spread any more."

MOUSE

Hilda Conkling

Little Mouse in gray velvet,
Have you had a cheese-breakfast?
There are no crumbs on your coat,
Did you use a napkin?
I wonder what you had to eat,
And who dresses you in gray velvet?

THE RABBIT

Edith King

Brown bunny sits inside his burrow
   Till everything is still,
Then out he slips along the furrow,
   Or up the grassy hill.

He nibbles all about the bushes
   Or sits to wash his face,
But at a sound he stamps, and rushes
   At a surprising pace.

You see some little streaks and flashes,
   A last sharp twink of white,
As down his hidy-hole he dashes
   And disappears from sight.

THE RABBIT

Georgia Roberts Durston

The rabbit has a habit
   Of sitting on his heels
With his little paws in front of him;
   I wonder how it feels.

The grasses where he passes
   He nibbles if they suit,
And he nips the tips of daisies,
   Or he chews a tender root.

He rollicks and he frolics
   In a very cunning way;
When the moon shines white upon him;
   But he loves to sleep by day.

His hole is where the mole is:
   Down beneath the maple tree;
Twisting in and out and round about,
   As safe as it can be.

THE RABBIT

Elizabeth Madox Roberts

When they said the time to hide was mine,
I hid back under a thick grapevine.

And while I was still for the time to pass,
A little gray thing came out of the grass.

He hopped his way through the melon bed
And sat down close by a cabbage head.

He sat down close where I could see,
And his big still eyes looked hard at me,

His big eyes bursting out of the rim,
And I looked back very hard at him.

A STORY IN THE SNOW

Pearl R. Crouch

This morning, as I walked to school
  Across the fluffy snow,
I came upon a bunny's tracks —
  A jumping, zigzag row.

He must have hurried very fast,
  For here and there I saw
Along his jerky, winding trail
  The print of Rover's paw!

I set my lunch pail on the snow
  And stood there very still,
For only Rover's clumsy tracks
  Led down the little hill.

Then suddenly I thought I heard
  A rustling sound close by;
And there within a grassy clump
  Shone Bunny's twinkling eye!

RABBITS

Dorothy Baruch

My two white rabbits
Chase each other
With humping, bumping backs.
   They go hopping, hopping,
   And their long ears
      Go flopping, flopping.
         And they
         Make faces
         With their noses
         Up and down.

Today
I went inside their fence
To play rabbit with them.
And in one corner
Under a loose bush
I saw something shivering the leaves.
And I pushed
And looked.
And I found —
There
In a hole
In the ground —
Three baby rabbits
Hidden away
        And *they*

Made faces
With their noses
Up and down.

POOR ROBIN

Mother Goose

The north wind doth blow,
And we shall have snow,
And what will poor Robin do then, poor thing?
He'll sit in the barn,
And keep himself warm,
And hide his head under his wing, poor thing!

MRS. PECK-PIGEON

Eleanor Farjeon

Mrs. Peck-Pigeon
Is picking for bread,
Bob — bob — bob
Goes her little round head.
Tame as a pussy cat
In the street,
Step — step — step
Go her little red feet.

With her little red feet
And her little round head,
Mrs. Peck-Pigeon
Goes picking for bread.

INVITATION

Harry Behn

Bluejay, fly to my windowsill!
Here's suet and raisins, so eat your fill.
Not that I care for your scratchy call,
And I like your manners least of all,
But when you are hungry, the chickadees
Who ask politely, please, please, please,
Are much too bothered by what you say —
So come have your breakfast, and fly away!

THE SNOW-BIRD

Frank Dempster Sherman

When all the ground with snow is white,
    The merry snow-bird comes,
And hops about with great delight
    To find the scattered crumbs.

How glad he seems to get to eat
   A piece of cake or bread!
He wears no shoes upon his feet,
   Nor hat upon his head.

But happiest is he, I know,
   Because no cage with bars
Keeps him from walking on the snow
   And printing it with stars.

THE SECRET

Unknown

We have a secret, just we three,
The robin, and I, and the sweet cherry-tree;
The bird told the tree, and the tree told me,
And nobody knows it but just us three.

But of course the robin knows it best,
Because he built the — I shan't tell the rest;
And laid the four little — something in it —
I'm afraid I shall tell it every minute.

But if the tree and the robin don't peep,
I'll try my best the secret to keep;
Though I know when the little birds fly about
Then the whole secret will be out.

A BIRD CAME DOWN THE WALK

Emily Dickinson

A bird came down the walk:
He did not know I saw;
He bit an angle-worm in halves
And ate the fellow, raw.

And then he drank a dew
From a convenient grass,
And then hopped sidewise to the wall
To let a beetle pass.

He glanced with rapid eyes
That hurried all abroad —
They looked like frightened beads, I thought
He stirred his velvet head

Like one in danger; cautious,
I offered him a crumb,
And he unrolled his feathers
And rowed him softer home

Than oars divide the ocean,
Too silver for a seam,
Or butterflies, off banks of noon,
Leap, plashless, as they swim.

CRUMBS

Walter de la Mare

You hungry birds, I bring my crumbs,
For now the cold of winter comes.
The North Wind blows down frozen rain;
The fields are white with snow again;
The worm's in house; the bare-twigged trees
Are thick with frost instead of bees;
From running brooks all noise is gone;
And every pool lies still as stone.

THE BIRD'S NEST

John Drinkwater

I know a place, in the ivy on a tree,
Where a bird's nest is, and the eggs are
    three;
And the bird is brown, and the eggs are
    blue,
And the twigs are old, but the moss is new;
And I go quite near, though I think
    I should have heard
The sound of me watching if
    I had been a bird.

66

PEOPLE BUY A LOT OF THINGS

Annette Wynne

People buy a lot of things —
Carts and balls and nails and rings,
But I would buy a bird that sings.

I would buy a bird that sings and let it sing for me,
And let it sing of flying things and mating in a tree,
And then I'd open wide the cage, and set the singer free.

SING LITTLE BIRD

Maria Hastings

Sing, little bird,
  when the skies are blue;
Sing, for the world
  has need of you;
Sing, when the skies
  are overcast;
Sing when the rain
  is falling fast.

Sing, happy heart,
  when the sun is warm;

67

Wing in the winter's
      coldest storm;
Sing little songs,
      O heart so true,
Sing for the world
      has need of you.

BE LIKE THE BIRD

Victor Hugo

Be like the bird, who
Halting in his flight
On limb too slight
Feels it give way beneath him,
Yet sings
Knowing he hath wings.

THE SQUIRREL

Unknown

Whisky, frisky,
Hippity hop,
Up he goes
To the tree top!

Whirly, twirly,
Round and round,
Down he scampers
To the ground.

Furly, curly,
What a tail!
Tall as a feather
Broad as a sail!

Where's his supper?
In the shell,
Snappity, crackity,
Out it fell.

LITTLE CHARLIE CHIPMUNK

Helen C. LeCron

Little Charlie Chipmunk was a *talker*. Mercy me!
He chattered after breakfast and he chattered after tea!
He chattered to his father and he chattered to his mother!
He chattered to his sister and he chattered to his brother!
He chattered till his family was almost driven *wild!*
Oh, little Charlie Chipmunk was a *very* tiresome child!

THE SKUNK

Dorothy Baruch

You'd better be
Nice to me.

If you're not
I will spit
Spat
Spout
And spray
All about

And you'll
Blink
And shrink
Screech
Scream
And shout,
"Stunky
Skunk
Get out!"

. . . But I won't . . .

SNAIL

John Drinkwater

Snail upon the wall,
Have you got at all
Anything to tell
About your shell?

Only this, my child —
When the wind is wild,
Or when the sun is hot,
It's all I've got.

DOWN IN THE HOLLOW

Aileen Fisher

Down in the hollow,
not so far away,
I saw a little ladybug
when I went to play,

Swinging on a clover
high in the air . . .
I wonder if the ladybug
knew that I was there.

71

NOTICE

David McCord

I have a dog,
I had a cat.
I've got a frog
Inside my hat.

WAKE UP! WAKE UP!

Bashō

Wake up! Wake up! It's I,
who want you for companion,
sleeping butterfly!

FUZZY WUZZY, CREEPY CRAWLY

Lillian Schulz Vanada

Fuzzy wuzzy, creepy crawly
Caterpillar funny,
You will be a butterfly
When the days are sunny.

Winging, flinging, dancing, springing
   Butterfly so yellow,
You were once a caterpillar,
   Wiggly, wiggly fellow.

THE CATERPILLAR

Christina Rossetti

      Brown and furry
      Caterpillar in a hurry:
      Take your walk
      To the shady leaf, or stalk.

      May no toad spy you,
      May the little birds pass by you;
      Spin and die,
      To live again a butterfly.

FORGIVEN

A. A. Milne

I found a little beetle, so that Beetle was his name,
And I called him Alexander and he answered just the same.
I put him in a match-box, and I kept him all the day . . .
And Nanny let my beetle out —

73

Yes, Nanny let my beetle out —
   She went and let my beetle out —
      And Beetle ran away.

She said she didn't mean it, and I never said she did,
She said she wanted matches and she just took off the lid,
She said that she was sorry, but it's difficult to catch
An excited sort of beetle you've mistaken for a match.

She said that she was sorry, and I really mustn't mind,
As there's lots and lots of beetles which she's certain we could
   find,
If we looked about the garden for the holes where beetles
   hid —
And we'd get another match-box and write BEETLE on the
   lid.

We went to all the places which a beetle might be near,
And we made the sort of noises which a beetle likes to hear,
And I saw a kind of something, and I gave a sort of shout:
"A beetle-house and Alexander Beetle coming out!"

It was Alexander Beetle I'm as certain as can be
And he had a sort of look as if he thought it must be ME,
And he had a sort of look as if he thought he ought to say:
"I'm very very sorry that I tried to run away."

And Nanny's very sorry too for you-know-what-she-did,
And she's writing ALEXANDER very blackly on the lid.
So Nan and Me are friends, because it's difficult to catch
An excited Alexander you've mistaken for a match.

THE FIREFLY LIGHTS HIS LAMP

Unknown (Japanese)

> Although the night is damp,
> The little firefly ventures out,
> And slowly lights his lamp.

THE DRAGONFLY

Chisoku

> The dragonfly:
>   his face is very nearly
>   only eye!

FIREFLIES

Aileen Fisher

> In the soft dark night
> when the wind is still
> and bullfrogs croak
> at the bottom of the hill,
> the fireflies reach
> inside their coat pockets
> and screw little light-bulbs

into their sockets
so they can fly
through the night and play
without bumping their heads
or losing their way.

LITTLE BUSY BEE

Isaac Watts

How doth the little busy bee
   Improve each shining hour,
And gather honey all the day
   From every opening flower!

How skillfully she builds her cell,
   How neat she spreads the wax,
And labors hard to store it well
   With the sweet food she makes!

CICADA-SHELL

Bashō

> Did it yell
>   till it became *all* voice?
>   Cicada-shell!

GRASSHOPPER GREEN

Unknown

Grasshopper green is a comical chap;
   He lives on the best of fare.
Bright little trousers, jacket, and cap,
   These are his summer wear.
Out in the meadow he loves to go,
   Playing away in the sun;
It's hopperty, skipperty, high and low,
   Summer's the time for fun.

Grasshopper green has a quaint little house;
   It's under the hedge so gay.
Grandmother Spider, as still as a mouse,
   Watches him over the way.
Gladly he's calling the children, I know,
   Out in the beautiful sun;
It's hopperty, skipperty, high and low,
   Summer's the time for fun.

77

THE OCTOPUS

Ogden Nash

Tell me, O Octopus, I begs,
Is those things arms, or is they legs?
I marvel at thee, Octopus;
If I were thou, I'd call me Us.

THE OCTOPUSSYCAT

Kenyon Cox

I love Octopussy, his arms are so long;
There's nothing in nature so sweet as his song.
'Tis true I'd not touch him — no, not for a farm!
If I keep at a distance he'll do me no harm.

THE WHALE

Buson

A whale!
Down it goes, and more and more
up goes its tail!

THE OLD POND

Bashō

> The old pond.
> A frog jumps in.
> The sound of water.

A BIG TURTLE

Unknown

> A big turtle sat on the end of a log,
> Watching a tadpole turn into a frog.

THE LITTLE TURTLE

Vachel Lindsay

> There was a little turtle.
> He lived in a box.
> He swam in a puddle.
> He climbed on the rocks.

79

He snapped at a mosquito.
He snapped at a flea.
He snapped at a minnow.
And he snapped at me.

He caught the mosquito.
He caught the flea.
He caught the minnow.
But he didn't catch me.

IF YOU SHOULD MEET A CROCODILE

Unknown

If you should meet a Crocodile
   Don't take a stick and poke him;
Ignore the welcome in his smile,
   Be careful not to stroke him.
For as he sleeps upon the Nile,
   He thinner gets and thinner;
And whene'er you meet a Crocodile
   He's ready for his dinner.

THE DINOSAUR

Carl S. Junge

> The Dinosaur,
> A beast of yore,
> Doesn't live here
> Any more.

HOLDING HANDS

Lenore M. Link

> Elephants walking
> Along the trails
>
> Are holding hands
> By holding tails.
>
> Trunks and tails
> Are handy things
>
> When elephants walk
> In Circus rings.

Elephants work
And elephants play

And elephants walk
And feel so gay.

And when they walk —
It never fails

They're holding hands
By holding tails.

THE ELEPHANT

Herbert Asquith

Here comes the elephant
Swaying along
With his cargo of children
All singing a song:
To the tinkle of laughter
He goes on his way,
And his cargo of children
Have crowned him with may.
His legs are in leather
And padded his toes:
He can root up an oak
With a whisk of his nose:

With a wave of his trunk
And a turn of his chin
He can pull down a house,
Or pick up a pin.
Beneath his gray forehead
A little eye peers;
Of what is he thinking
Between those wide ears?

THE ELEPHANT'S TRUNK

Alice Wilkins

The elephant always carries his trunk.
I couldn't do that with my own.
His trunk is a part of himself, you see —
It's part of his head — it's grown!

THE PLAINT OF THE CAMEL

Charles Edward Carryl

Canary-birds feed on sugar and seed,
    Parrots have crackers to crunch;
And, as for the poodles, they tell me the noodles
    Have chickens and cream for their lunch.
    But there's never a question
    About *my* digestion—
    Anything does for me!

Cats, you're aware, can repose in a chair,
　　Chickens can roost upon rails;
Puppies are able to sleep in a stable,
　　And oysters can slumber in pails.
　　But no one supposes
　　A poor Camel dozes —
　　Any place does for me!

Lambs are enclosed where it's never exposed,
　　Coops are constructed for hens;
Kittens are treated to houses well heated,
　　And pigs are protected by pens.
　　But a Camel comes handy
　　Wherever it's sandy —
　　Anywhere does for me!

People would laugh if you rode a giraffe,
　　Or mounted the back of an ox;
It's nobody's habit to ride on a rabbit,
　　Or try to bestraddle a fox.
　　But as for a Camel, he's
　　Ridden by families —
　　Any load does for me!

A snake is as round as a hole in the ground,
　　And weasels are wavy and sleek;
And no alligator could ever be straighter
　　Than lizards that live in a creek.
　　But a Camel's all lumpy
　　And bumpy and humpy —
　　Any shape does for me!

84

GRIZZLY BEAR

Mary Austin

If you ever, ever, ever meet a grizzly bear,
You must never, never, never ask him *where*
He is going,
Or *what* he is doing;
For if you ever, ever, dare
To stop a grizzly bear,
You will never meet *another* grizzly bear.

JUMP OR JINGLE

Evelyn Beyer

Frogs jump
Caterpillars hump

Worms wiggle
Bugs jiggle

Rabbits hop
Horses clop

Snakes slide
Seagulls glide

Mice creep
Deer leap

Puppies bounce
Kittens pounce

Lions stalk —
But —
I walk!

THE KANGAROO

Unknown

Old Jumpety-Bumpety-Hop-and-Go-One
Was lying asleep on his side in the sun.
This old kangaroo, he was whisking the flies
(With his long glossy tail) from his ears and his eyes.
Jumpety-Bumpety-Hop-and-Go-One
Was lying asleep on his side in the sun,
Jumpety-Bumpety-Hop!

GOOD MORNING

Muriel Sipe

One day I saw a downy duck,
With feathers on his back;
I said, "Good morning, downy duck,"
And he said, "Quack, quack, quack."

One day I saw a timid mouse,
He was so shy and meek;
I said, "Good morning, timid mouse,"
And he said, "Squeak, squeak, squeak."

One day I saw a curly dog,
I met him with a bow;
I said, "Good morning, curly dog,"
And he said, "Bow-wow-wow."

One day I saw a scarlet bird,
He woke me from my sleep;
I said, "Good morning, scarlet bird,"
And he said, "Cheep, cheep, cheep."

HURT NO LIVING THING

Christina Rossetti

Hurt no living thing:
    Ladybird, no butterfly,
Nor moth with dusty wing,
    No cricket chirping cheerily,
Nor grasshopper so light of leap,
    Nor dancing gnat, nor beetle fat,
Nor harmless worms that creep.

THE ANIMAL STORE

Rachel Field

If I had a hundred dollars to spend,
    Or maybe a little more,
I'd hurry as fast as my legs would go
    Straight to the animal store.

I wouldn't say, "How much for this or that?" —
    "What kind of a dog is he?"
I'd buy as many as rolled an eye,
    Or wagged a tail at me!

I'd take the hound with the drooping ears
   That sits by himself alone;
Cockers and Cairns and wobbly pups
   For to be my very own.

I might buy a parrot all red and green,
   And the monkey I saw before,
If I had a hundred dollars to spend,
   Or maybe a little more.

KINDNESS TO ANIMALS

Unknown

Little children, never give
Pain to things that feel and live;
Let the gentle robin come
For the crumbs you save at home, —
As his meat you throw along
He'll repay you with a song;
Never hurt the timid hare
Peeping from her green grass lair,
Let her come and sport and play
On the lawn at close of day;
Little lark goes soaring high
To the bright windows of the sky,
Singing as if 'twere always spring,
And fluttering on an untired wing, —
Oh! let him sing his happy song,
Nor do these gentle creatures wrong.

From
Day
To
Day

BEDTIME

Eleanor Farjeon

Five minutes, five minutes more, please!
  Let me stay five minutes more!
Can't I just finish the castle
  I'm building here on the floor?
Can't I just finish the story
  I'm reading here in my book?
Can't I just finish this bead-chain —
  It *almost* is finished, look!
Can't I just finish this game, please?
  When a game's once begun
It's a pity never to find out
  Whether you've lost or won.
Can't I just stay five minutes?
  Well, can't I stay just four?
Three minutes, then? two minutes?
  Can't I stay *one* minute more?

THE CRITIC

John Farrar

Sometimes when it is bedtime,
  My mother comes to me,

92

She takes me from my warm bed,
And sits me on her knee.

And it is very pleasant
To hear her golden voice,
Reading bedtime stories
According to my choice.

And when she reads me poems,
The kind that I like best —
The music of them lulls me
Quite gently to my rest.

Now, often when I'm wakeful
I count a million sheep —
But poems are far, far better
For putting boys to sleep!

GOOD NIGHT

Thomas Hood

Here's a body — there's a bed!
There's a pillow — here's a head!
There's a curtain — here's a light!
There's a puff — and so good night!

I SEE THE MOON

Unknown

> I see the moon,
> And the moon sees me;
> God bless the moon,
> And God bless me.

NOW I LAY ME

Unknown

> Now I lay me down to sleep,
> I pray thee, Lord, my soul to keep;
> Thy love stay with me through the night
> And wake me with the morning light.
> > Amen.

MY BED

Lucy Sprague Mitchell

> I have a little bed
> Just for me.
> Brother's too big for it,

Mummy's too big for it.
Daddy's too big for it.
Do you see?

I have a little bed,
Do you see?
But — pussy's too small for it.
Puppy's too small for it.
Baby's too small for it.
It's just for me.

TWO IN BED

Abram Bunn Ross

When my brother Tommy
Sleeps in bed with me,
He doubles up
And makes
himself
exactly
like
a
V

And 'cause the bed is not so wide,
A part of him is on my side.

COUNTING SHEEP

Aileen Fisher

Mother says
to go to sleep

I should try
to count some sheep.

But then I'd have
to stay awake

To keep from making
a mistake.

SNORING

Aileen Fisher

I often have to wonder
how Father, at night,
can snore so loud
and yet sleep so tight:
I should think his Snorings
would keep him awake
every single minute
with the noises they make.

THE CLOCK

Jean Jaszi

At night the ticking of the clock
Is twice as loud as in the day;
I think he wants to tell me
That he isn't far away.

For when it's daylight
I can see him;
When it's night
I only hear him.

Tick-tock, tick-tock,
It's a cozy sound at night.

KEEP A POEM IN YOUR POCKET

Beatrice Schenk de Regniers

Keep a poem in your pocket
and a picture in your head
and you'll never feel lonely
at night when you're in bed.

The little poem will sing to you
the little picture bring to you
a dozen dreams to dance to you
at night when you're in bed.

So —
Keep a poem in your pocket
and a picture in your head
and you'll never feel lonely
at night when you're in bed.

SOFTLY, DROWSILY

Walter de la Mare

Softly, drowsily,
Out of sleep;
Into the world again
Ann's eyes peep;
Over the pictures
Across the walls
One little quivering
Sunbeam falls.
A thrush in the garden
Seems to say,
Wake, Little Ann,
'Tis day, 'tis day;
Faint sweet breezes
The casement stir
Breathing of pinks

And lavender,
At last from her pillow,
With cheeks bright red,
Up comes her round little
Tousled head;
And out she tumbles
From her warm bed.

GOOD NIGHT

Victor Hugo

Good night! Good night!
Far flies the light;
But still God's love
Shall flame above,
Making all bright.
Good night! Good night!

THE BIG CLOCK

Unknown

Slowly ticks the big clock;
Tick-tock, tick-tock!
But Cuckoo clock ticks double quick;
Tick-a-tock-a, tick-a-tock-a,
Tick-a-tock-a, tick!

THE TOASTER

William Jay Smith

A silver-scaled dragon with jaws flaming red
Sits at my elbow and toasts my bread.
I hand him fat slices, and then, one by one
He hands them back when he sees they are done.

INDIAN CHILDREN

Annette Wynne

Where we walk to school each day
Indian children used to play —
All about our native land,
Where the shops and houses stand.

And the trees were very tall,
And there were no streets at all,
Not a church and not a steeple —
Only woods and Indian people.

Only wigwams on the ground,
And at nights bears prowling round —
What a different place today
Where we live and work and play!

A LITTLE BIRD

Aileen Fisher

"What do you have for breakfast?"
I asked a little bird,
"Orange juice and cereal?"
He didn't say a word.
He merely ate a flower seed
and something from a limb
which might, I guess, be cereal
and orange juice — for him!

THE PACKAGE

Aileen Fisher

There's a package,
there's a package,
there's a package in the mail.
It's wrapped in yellow paper
and the twine is like a tail.
Three stamps are in the corner,
and the writing's rather pale —
there's a package,
there's a package,
there's a package in the mail.

It's for Mother,
it's for Mother,
it's for Mother, I can see.
But that is just about as good
as knowing it's for me,
for Mother'll say, "Come, open it,
untie the string and see."
There's a package,
there's a package,
oh, what CAN the package be?

IN MY NEW CLOTHING

Bashō

In my new clothing
I feel so different
I must
Look like someone else

NEWSPAPER

Aileen Fisher

I always hope Father is going to play,
with the paper in front of his face that way.

I think he might look from the edge and wink
or peekaboo me, but what do you think:

He reads all the pages from A to Z
and never once thinks of being Daddy to me.

AUTOMOBILE MECHANICS

Dorothy Baruch

Sometimes
  I help my dad
Work on our automobile.
    We unscrew
    The radiator cap
      And we let some water run —
      Swish — from a hose
      Into the tank.

      And then we open up the hood
      And feed in oil
      From a can with a long spout.
      And then we take a lot of rags
      And clean all about.
        We clean the top
        And the doors
        And the fenders and the wheels
        And the windows and floors . . .
          We work *hard*
          My dad
          And I.

THE WORKSHOP

Aileen Fisher

Father has a workshop
with a table and a scale
and a cupboard full of cubbies
for every kind of nail,
and a hammer and a hatchet
and an anvil and a brace . . .
and Father seems to know the minute things
              are out of place!

Father has a grindstone
that wobbles in its frame,
and he has a sort of pickaxe
with a very funny name,
and a wood rasp and a chisel
and a sickle for the lawn . . .
and Father seems to know the minute anything
              is gone!

LAWN-MOWER

Dorothy Baruch

I'm the gardener today.
I push the lawn-mower

Across the grass.
  Zwuzz, wisssh, zwuzz, wisssh.

I'm the lawn's barber.
I'm cutting
Its green hair
  Short.

I push the lawn-mower
Across the grass.
  Zwuzz, wisssh.

SNEEZING

Marie Louise Allen

  Air comes in tickly
  Through my nose,
  Then very quickly —
  Out it goes:
  Ahhh — CHOO!

  With every sneeze
  I have to do,
  I make a breeze —
  Ahh — CHOO! — Ahh — CHOO!

MUMPS

Elizabeth Madox Roberts

I had a feeling in my neck,
    And on the sides were two big bumps;
I couldn't swallow anything
    At all because I had the mumps.

And Mother tied it with a piece.
    And then she tied up Will and John,
And no one else but Dick was left
    That didn't have a mump rag on.

He teased at us and laughed at us,
    And said, whenever he went by,
"It's vinegar and lemon drops
    And pickles!" just to make us cry.

But Tuesday Dick was very sad
    And cried because his neck was sore,
And not a one said sour things
    To anybody any more.

THE MITTEN SONG

Marie Louise Allen

"Thumbs in the thumb-place,
Fingers all together!"
This is the song
We sing in mitten-weather.
When it is cold,
It doesn't matter whether
Mittens are wool,
Or made of finest leather.
This is the song
We sing in mitten-weather:
"Thumbs in the thumb-place,
Fingers all together!"

TUMMY ACHE

Aileen Fisher

Father said that maybe
it was too much candy.

Mother said more likely
it was gooseberry jam.

107

Father said that maybe
with the sweet things handy
I forgot my gravy
and vegetables
and ham.

Mother said that prob'ly
I had been too gobbly.

Father nodded "probably"
and so did Gram.

But I said "Certainly,
it COULDN'T have been candy . . .
it must have been the gravy
and vegetables
and ham."

WALKING

Grace Ellen Glaubitz

When Daddy
Walks
With Jean and me,
We have a
Lot of fun
'Cause we can't
Walk as fast
As he,

Unless we
Skip and
Run!
I stretch,
And stretch
My legs so far,
I nearly slip
and fall —
But how
Does Daddy
Take such steps?
He doesn't stretch
At all!

SHOES

Tom Robinson

My father has a pair of shoes
So beautiful to see!
I want to wear my father's shoes,
They are too big for me.

My baby brother has a pair,
As cunning as can be!
My feet won't go into that pair,
They are too small for me.

There's only one thing I can do
Till I get small or grown.
If I want to have a fitting shoe,
I'll have to wear my own.

GALOSHES

Rhoda W. Bacmeister

Susie's galoshes
Make splishes and sploshes
And slooshes and sloshes,
As Susie steps slowly
Along in the slush.

They stamp and they tramp
On the ice and concrete,
They get stuck in the muck and the mud;
But Susie likes much best to hear

The slippery slush
As it slooshes and sloshes,
And splishes and sploshes,
All round her galoshes!

NEW SHOES

Marjorie S. Watts

When I am walking down the street
I do so like to watch my feet.
Perhaps you do not know the news,

110

Mother has bought me fine new shoes!
When the left one steps I do not speak,
I listen to its happy squeak.

CHOOSING SHOES

Ffrida Wolfe

New shoes, new shoes,
　　Red and pink and blue shoes.
Tell me, what would *you* choose,
　　If they'd let us buy?

Buckle shoes, bow shoes,
　　Pretty pointy-toe shoes,
Strappy, cappy low shoes;
　　Let's have some to try.

Bright shoes, white shoes,
　　Dandy-dance-by-night shoes,
Perhaps-a-little-tight shoes,
　　Like some? So would I.

　　　　But

Flat shoes, fat shoes,
　　Stump-along-like-that shoes,
Wipe-them-on-the-mat shoes,
　　That's the sort they'll buy.

111

RAIN SIZES

John Ciardi

Rain comes in various sizes.
Some rain is as small as a mist.
It tickles your face with surprises,
And tingles as if you'd been kissed.

Some rain is the size of a sprinkle
And doesn't put out all the sun.
You can see the drops sparkle and twinkle,
And a rainbow comes out when it's done.

Some rain is as big as a nickle
And comes with a crash and a hiss.
It comes down too heavy to tickle.
It's more like a splash than a kiss.

When it rains the right size and you're wrapped in
Your rainclothes, it's fun out of doors.
But run home before you get trapped in
The big rain that rattles and roars.

THE UMBRELLA BRIGADE

Laura E. Richards

"Pitter patter!" falls the rain
On the school-room window-pane.
Such a plashing! such a dashing!
Will it e'er be dry again?
Down the gutter rolls a flood,
And the crossing's deep in mud;
And the puddles! oh, the puddles
Are a sight to stir one's blood!

> *Chorus:* But let it rain
> Tree-toads and frogs,
> Muskets and pitchforks,
> Kittens and dogs!
> Dash away! plash away!
> Who is afraid?
> Here we go,
> The Umbrella Brigade!

Pull the boots up to the knee!
Tie the hoods on merrily!
Such a hustling! such a jostling!
Out of breath with fun are we.
Clatter, clatter, down the street,
Greeting every one we meet,
With our laughing and our chaffing,
Which the laughing drops repeat.

Chorus: So let it rain
        Tree-toads and frogs,
        Muskets and pitchforks,
        Kittens and dogs!
        Dash away! plash away!
        Who is afraid?
        Here we go,
        The Umbrella Brigade!

OTHERS

Harry Behn

Even though it's raining
I don't wish it wouldn't.
That would be like saying
I think it shouldn't.
I'd rather be out playing
Than sitting hours and hours
Watching rain falling
In drips and drops and showers,
But what about the robins?
What about the flowers?

SATURDAY SHOPPING

Katherine Edelman

To market, to market,
On Saturday morn,
For prunes and potatoes
And ears of sweet corn,
For bacon and sausage,
For apple and pear.
To market, to market —
Our cupboard is bare!

SHOP WINDOWS

Rose Fyleman

Mother likes the frocks and hats
And pretty stuffs and coloured mats.

Daddy never, never looks
At anything but pipes and books.

Auntie's fond of chains and rings
And all the sparkly diamond things.

Richard likes machines the best;
He doesn't care about the rest.

115

Nanny always loves to stop
In front of every single shop.

But I don't want to wait for a minute
Till we get to the one with the puppy dogs in it.

PUSHCART ROW

Rachel Field

In rain or shine; in heat or snow;
The pushcarts stretch in a long green row,
Close to the curb as they can crowd,
With men all shouting their wares aloud.
If you have need of a lettuce head,
Or a bunch of radishes shiny red,
Of onions, carrots, or cauliflower,
Oranges sweet or lemons sour,
Polished apples or dripping greens,
Fat little mushrooms, thin string beans.
Of fruits and berries plump and round,
By the basket, by the pound —
Bring out your purse and take your pick
Where the two-wheeled pushcarts cluster thick;
Where dogs and children play about
Wheels and pavement and gutter-spout;
Where the women wear shawls and earrings gold
And the men are mostly brown and old
With selling their wares in shine or snow
On the cobblestones of Pushcart Row.

COUNTERS

Elizabeth Coatsworth

To think I once saw grocery shops
    With but a casual eye
And fingered figs and apricots
    As one who came to buy!

To think I never dreamed of how
    Bananas swayed in the rain,
And often looked at oranges,
    Yet never thought of Spain!

And in those wasted days I saw
    No sails above the tea —
For grocery shops were grocery shops,
    Not hemispheres to me!

WHEN I WAS LOST

Dorothy Aldis

Underneath my belt
My stomach was a stone.
Sinking was the way I felt.
And hollow.
And Alone.

VEGETABLES

Rachel Field

A carrot has a green fringed top;
  A beet is royal red;
And lettuces are curious,
  All curled and run to head.

Some beans have strings to tie them on,
  And, what is still more queer,
Ripe corn is nothing more or less
  Than one enormous ear!

But when potatoes all have eyes,
  Why is it they should be
Put in the ground and covered up —
  Where it's too dark to see?

ANIMAL CRACKERS

Christopher Morley

Animal crackers, and cocoa to drink,
That is the finest of suppers, I think;
When I'm grown up and can have what I please
I think I shall always insist upon these.

What do *you* choose when you're offered a treat?
When Mother says, "What would you like best to eat?"
Is it waffles and syrup, or cinnamon toast?
It's cocoa and animals that I love most!

The kitchen's the cosiest place that I know:
The kettle is singing, the stove is aglow,
And there in the twilight, how jolly to see
The cocoa and animals waiting for me.

Daddy and Mother dine later in state,
With Mary to cook for them, Susan to wait;
But they don't have nearly as much fun as I
Who eat in the kitchen with Nurse standing by;
And Daddy once said, he would like to be me
Having cocoa and animals once more for tea!

A PARTY

Laura E. Richards

On Willy's birthday, as you see,
These little boys have come to tea.
But, oh! how very sad to tell!
They have not been behaving well.
For ere they took a single bite,
They all began to scold and fight.

The little boy whose name was Ned,
He wanted jelly on his bread;
The little boy whose name was Sam,
He vowed he would have damson jam;
The little boy whose name was Phil
Said, "I'll have honey! *Yes*—I—WILL!!'"

BUT—
The little boy whose name was Paul,
While they were quarrelling, ate it all.

GROWING UP

Harry Behn

When I was seven
We went for a picnic
Up to a magic
Forestry place.
I knew there were tigers
Behind every boulder,
Though I didn't meet one
Face to face.

When I was older
We went for a picnic
Up to the very same
Place as before,
And all of the trees

And the rocks were so little
They couldn't hide tigers
Or *me* any more.

A PICNIC

Aileen Fisher

We had a picnic.
We had buns.
We had wieners —
big fat ones.
We had wieners
on a stick . . .
Mother told us:
"Don't be quick,
Turn your wieners
front and back,
cook them slowly
till they crack."

We had cookies
and lemonade.
Beth saw a bee
and got afraid.
I dropped a pickle
in the dirt,
but I washed it off

so it didn't hurt.
We had a picnic.
Was it fun!
NOW all we want
is another one!

PICNIC DAY

Rachel Field

Sing a song of picnics,
   Bread and butter spread,
Greenery all around about,
   And cherries overhead!

A PARADE

Mary Catherine Rose

A parade! A parade!
A-rum-a-tee-tum
I know a parade
By the sound of the drum.
   A-rum-a-tee-tum
   A-rum-a-tee-tum
   A-rum-a-tee-tum-a-tee-tum-
   a-tee-tum.
Here it comes

Down the street.
I know a parade
By the sound of the feet.

Music and feet
Music and feet
Can't you feel
The sound and the beat?
   A-rum-a-tee-tum
   A-rum-a-tee-tum
   A-rum-a-tee-tum-a-tee-tum-
   a-tee-tum.

C IS FOR THE CIRCUS

Phyllis McGinley

C is for the Circus
   Which springtime brings to town.
(The country has its crocus,
   But we much prefer the clown.)
C's for canes and cracker-jack
   And curious camels, too.
I wouldn't trade a Circus
   For some crocuses, Would you?

A CIRCUS GARLAND

Rachel Field

Parade

This is the day the circus comes
With blare of brass, with beating drums,
And clashing cymbals, and with roar
Of wild beasts never heard before
Within town limits. Spick and span
Will shine each gilded cage and van;
Cockades at every horse's head
Will nod, and riders dressed in red
Or blue trot by. There will be floats
In shapes like dragons, thrones and boats,
And clowns on stilts; freaks big and small,
Till leisurely and last of all
Camels and elephants will pass
Beneath our elms, along our grass.

The Performing Seal

Who is so proud
As not to feel
A secret awe
Before a seal
That keeps such sleek
And wet repose
While twirling candles
On his nose?

124

Acrobat

Surely that is not a man
    Balanced on a thread in air,
But a brightly colored fan
    Folding and unfolding there?

The Elephant

With wrinkled hide and great frayed ears,
Gunga, the elephant, appears.
Colored like city smoke he goes
As gingerly on blunted toes
As if he held the earth in trust
And feared to hurt the very dust.

The Girl on the Milk-White Horse

See, they are clearing the sawdust course
For the girl in pink on the milk-white horse
Her spangles twinkle; his pale flanks shine,
Every hair of his tail is fine
And bright as a comet's; his mane blows free,
And she points a toe and bends a knee,
The while his hoofbeats fall like rain
Over and over and over again.
And nothing that moves on land or sea
Will seem so beautiful to me
As the girl in pink on the milk-white horse
Cantering over the sawdust course.

Next Day

Nothing now to mark the spot

But a littered vacant lot;
Sawdust in a heap, and there
Where the ring was, grass worn bare
In a circle, scuffed and brown,
And a paper hoop the clown
Made his little dog jump through,
And a pygmy pony-shoe.

THE CIRCUS PARADE

Olive Beaupré Miller

Tomorrow, tomorrow's the circus parade!
Just think what I shall see!
What crowds of people in gay colored clothes
All lined up the street there will be.

And some of the children will have red balloons,
As up by the curbing they stand,
Then off in the distance we'll suddenly hear
The circus's big brass band!

Behind the crash bang! of the music they play,
Come riders in red velvet gowns,
And after them doing the funniest things,
A silly procession of clowns.

Then the lions and tigers that pace up and down,
In wagons all painted with gold,
And monkeys a-playing just all kinds of tricks,
As they grimace and chatter and scold.

Oh, next there come camels and elephants, too,
With men on their backs astride,
And queer little ponies, no bigger than dogs,
And a donkey perhaps beside!

And then there come chariots rumbling by
With horses all four in a row;
And the wheezing, old calliope is
The very tail end of the show!

From MY BOOK HOUSE. Used by permission of the author and the publishers, THE BOOK HOUSE FOR CHILDREN.

MY HOUSE

Jane W. Krows

I have in my house
A door — a floor
A rug — a mug
A stool — a tool
A book — a nook
A stair — a chair
And I'll get
I bet — a pet.

People

Everywhere

THE PEOPLE

Elizabeth Madox Roberts

The ants are walking under the ground,
And the pigeons are flying on the steeple,
And in between are the people.

PEOPLE

Lois Lenski

Tall people, short people,
Thin people, fat,
Lady so dainty
Wearing a hat,
Straight people, dumpy people,
Man dressed in brown;
Baby in a buggy —
These make a town.

THE CUPBOARD

Walter de la Mare

I know a little cupboard,
With a teeny tiny key,
And there's a jar of Lollypops
   For me, me, me.

It has a little shelf, my dear,
As dark as dark can be,
And there's a dish of Banbury Cakes
   For me, me, me.

I have a small fat grandmamma,
With a very slippery knee,
And she's Keeper of the Cupboard,
   With the key, key, key.

And when I'm very good, my dear,
As good as good can be,
There's Banbury Cakes, and Lollypops
   For me, me, me.

THE NEW NEIGHBOR

Rose Fyleman

Have you had your tonsils out?
    Do you go to school?
Do you know that there are frogs
    Down by Willow Pool?

Are you good at cricket?
    Have you got a bat?
Do you know the proper way
    To feed a white rat?

Are there any apples
    On your apple tree?
Do you think your mother
    Will ask me in to tea?

VISITORS

Harry Behn

In winter when people pay a call
On us, they hurry inside our hall
And quickly shut the outside door
And slap their hands and stamp the floor,
And then they talk about the snow
For hours, until it's time to go.

Then, all wrapped up in their mufflers, they
Remember what they had meant to say.
They stand there in the open door
And start to remember more and more
While Mummy smiles and smiles, and freezes,
Till Daddy deliberately sneezes.

WELCOME

Rose Waldo

Little new neighbor, have you come to be
A playmate of mine from over the sea?
I'm glad you are here. Oh, won't it be fine
To learn all your games, and I'll teach you mine!
We won't understand all the words that we say,
But I'm sure that we both will know how to play.
So will you come now and swing while I swing,
And we'll sing all the songs that we love to sing.

TIRED TIM

Walter de la Mare

Poor tired Tim! It's sad for him.
He lags the long bright morning through,
Ever so tired of nothing to do;
He moons and mopes the livelong day,

133

Nothing to think about, nothing to say;
Up to bed with his candle to creep,
Too tired to yawn, too tired to sleep:
Poor tired Tim! It's sad for him.

MISS T.

Walter de la Mare

It's a very odd thing —
    As odd as can be —
That whatever Miss T. eats
    Turns into Miss T.;
Porridge and apples,
    Mince, muffins and mutton,
Jam, junket, jumbles —
    Not a rap, not a button
It matters; the moment
    They're out of her plate,
Though shared by Miss Butcher
    And sour Mr. Bate;
Tiny and cheerful,
    And neat as can be,
Whatever Miss T. eats
    Turns into Miss T.

P'S THE PROUD POLICEMAN

Phyllis McGinley

> P's the proud Policeman
>   With buttons polished neat.
> He's pleased to put his hand up
>   When you want to cross the street.
> By daylight he protects you;
>   He protects you through the dark,
> And he points the way politely
>   To the playground or the park.

BOBBY BLUE

John Drinkwater

> Sometimes I have to cross the road
>   When some one isn't there
> Except a man in uniform
>   Who takes a lot of care;
>
> I do not call him Officer
>   As other people do,
> I thank him most politely,
>   And call him Bobby Blue.

135

He's very big, and every one
   Does everything he tells,
The motor-cars with hooters
   And the bicycles with bells;

And even when I cross the road
   With other people too,
I always say as I go by,
   "Good-morning, Bobby Blue."

MY POLICEMAN

Rose Fyleman

He is always standing there
At the corner of the Square;
He is very big and fine
And his silver buttons shine.

All the carts and taxis do
Everything he tells them to,
And the little errand boys
When they pass him make no noise.

Though I seem so very small
I am not afraid at all;
He and I are friends, you see,
And he always smiles at me.

Once I wasn't very good
Rather near to where he stood,
But he never said a word
Though I'm sure he must have heard.

Nurse has a policeman too
(Hers has brown eyes, mine has blue),
Hers is sometimes on a horse,
But I like mine best of course.

THE POSTMAN

Laura E. Richards

Hey! the little postman,
  And his little dog.
Here he comes a-hopping
  Like a little frog;
Bringing me a letter,
  Bringing me a note,
In the little pocket
  Of his little coat.

Hey! the little postman,
  And his little bag,
Here he comes a-trotting
  Like a little nag;

Bringing me a paper,
   Bringing me a bill,
From the little grocer
   On the little hill.

Hey! the little postman,
   And his little hat,
Here he comes a-creeping
   Like a little cat.
What is that he's saying?
   "Naught for you to-day!"
Horrid little postman!
   I wish you'd go away!

BUSY CARPENTERS

James S. Tippett

The song of the saw
Is true
As we cut the boards
In two.

The song of the plane
Is sweet
As the shavings curl
At our feet.

And the song of the hammer
Is good
As we drive the nails
In the wood.

THE BARBER'S

Walter de la Mare

Gold locks, and black locks,
  Red locks and brown,
Topknot to love-curl
  The hair wisps down;
Straight above the clear eyes,
  Rounded round the ears,
Snip-snap and snick-a-snick,
  Clash the Barber's shears;
Us, in the looking-glass,
  Footsteps in the street,
Over, under, to and fro,
  The lean blades meet;
Bay Rum or Bear's Grease,
  A silver groat to pay —
Then out a-shin-shan-shining
  In the bright, blue day.

BARBER'S CLIPPERS

Dorothy Baruch

The barber snips and snips
My hair with his scissors
And then he zips on
His clippers.
    It clips
    Up and down
    And around
    My hair in back.

      Ssss ssss
      It swishes
      On the sides
      Behind my ears.

      Ssss ssss
      It tickles
      As it slides
         Straight up the middle
         Of my neck.

THE SHOEMAKER

Unknown

As I was a-walking the other day,
   I peeped in a window just over the way,
And old and bent and feeble too,
   There sat an old cobbler a-making a shoe.
With a rack-a-tac-tac and a rack-a-tac-too,
   This is the way he makes a shoe.
With a bright little awl he makes a hole,
   Right through the upper, and then through the sole.
He puts in a peg, he puts in two,
   And a ha-ha-ha-ha and he hammers it through.

THE COBBLER

Eleanor Alletta Chaffee

Crooked heels
   And scuffy toes
Are all the kinds
   Of shoes he knows.

He patches up
   The broken places,
Sews the seams
   And shines their faces.

141

THE DENTIST

Rose Fyleman

I'd like to be a dentist with a plate upon the door
And a little bubbling fountain in the middle of the floor;
With lots of tiny bottles all arranged in colored rows
And a page-boy with a line of silver buttons down his clothes.

I'd love to polish up the things and put them every day
Inside the darling chests of drawers all tidily away;
And every Sunday afternoon when nobody was there
I should go riding up and down upon the velvet chair.

ENGINEERS

Jimmy Garthwaite

Pistons, valves and wheels and gears
That's the life of engineers
Thumping, chunking engines going
Hissing steam and whistles blowing.

There's not a place I'd rather be
Than working round machinery
Listening to that clanking sound
Watching all the wheels go round.

THE FLOWER-CART MAN

Rachel Field

When it's just past April
  And going on May,
The bent old Flower Man
  Comes our way.

His clothes are very baggy,
  His horse is lean and gray,
But, like a walking garden,
  His cart with plants is gay.

All filled with nodding rose trees
  To make your parlor bright,
With tulips for your table,
  Or daisies gold and white.

With pansy plants and lilies,
  Primrose and daffodil,
And red geraniums in pots
  To trim your window sill.

Everywhere his cart goes
  The air smells sweet,
As the gray horse and he
  Jog from street to street.

They say that Spring's a lady
   And it may be so,
Though she never stopped on our street
   As far as I know —

But the bent old Flower Man
   Comes our way,
When it's just past April
   And going on May.

THE MILKMAN

Jane W. Krows

Clippity Clop, Clippity Clop,
I hear the horses tread.
It is the milkman bringing milk
While I am still in bed.

THE CLOWN

Mary Catherine Rose

The jolly old clown
Is funny and gay.
He laughs and sings
In the merriest way.

Of all the others
That are known to me,
A clown is what
I would like best to be.

THE BALLOON MAN

Rose Fyleman

He always comes on market days,
   And holds balloons — a lovely bunch —
And in the market square he stays,
   And never seems to think of lunch.

They're red and purple, blue and green,
   And when it is a sunny day
Tho' carts and people get between
   You see them shining far away.

And some are big and some are small,
   All tied together with a string,
And if there is a wind at all
   They tug and tug like anything.

Some day perhaps he'll let them go
   And we shall see them sailing high,
And stand and watch them from below —
   They *would* look pretty in the sky!

BALLOON MAN

Jessica N. North

Clustering rainbow-grapes
On a tight tether!
Beautiful bubble-shapes
Dancing together!

Oh, if you'd ask me
What life would be sweet,
I'd be balloon man
In Dorchester Street.

Pink ones on stormy days,
Blue ones on bright;
Green ones in winter-time,
Golden at night, —

All the wee children
Would cry in my train,
"Mr. Balloon Man,
Come quickly again!"

To every waiting heart
Comfort I'd bring,
Peddling joy
On the end of a string.

THE CIRCUS

Elizabeth Madox Roberts

Friday came and the circus was there
And Mother said that the twins and I
And Charles and Clarence and all of us
Could go out and see the parade go by.

And there were wagons with pictures on,
And you never could guess what they had inside,
Nobody could guess, for the doors were shut,
And there was a dog that a monkey could ride.

A man on the top of a sort of a cart
Was clapping his hands and making a talk.
And the elephant came — he can step pretty far —
It made us laugh to see him walk.

Three beautiful ladies came riding by,
And each one had on a golden dress,
And each one had a golden whip.
They were queens of Sheba, I guess.

A big wild man was in a cage,
And he had some snakes going over his feet
And somebody said, "He eats them alive!"
But I didn't see him eat.

THE PRETZEL MAN

Rachel Field

The Pretzel Man has a little stand
With spikes like the fingers on a hand,
And everyone strung up and down
With rings all baked to crispy brown.
The very richest queens and kings
Could never wear so many rings;
Though theirs be made of brightest gold
Set thick with jewels ages old —
Still, Pretzel Men can *eat* their rings
And this is not the case with kings!

THE ICE-CREAM MAN

Rachel Field

When summer's in the city,
   And brick's a blaze of heat,
The Ice-Cream Man with his little cart
   Goes trundling down the street.

Beneath his round umbrella,
   Oh, what a joyful sight,
To see him fill the cones with mounds
   Of cooling brown or white:

Vanilla, chocolate, strawberry,
    Or chilly things to drink
From bottles full of frosty-fizz,
    Green, orange, white, or pink.

His cart might be a flower bed
    Of roses and sweet peas,
The way the children cluster round
    As thick as honeybees.

GYPSY JANE

William Brighty Rands

She had corn flowers in her hair
    As she came up the lane;
"What may be your name, my dear?"
    "O, sir, Gypsy Jane."

"You are berry-brown, my dear."
    "That, sir, well may be,
For I live more than half the year,
    Under tent or tree."

Shine, Sun! Blow, Wind!
    Fall gently, Rain!
The year's declined; be soft and kind,
    Kind to Gypsy Jane.

THE PEDDLER'S CARAVAN

William Brighty Rands

I wish I lived in a caravan,
With a horse to drive, like a peddler-man!
Where he comes from nobody knows,
Or where he goes to, but on he goes!

His caravan has windows two,
And a chimney of tin, that the smoke comes through;
He has a wife, with a baby brown,
And they go riding from town to town.

Chairs to mend, and delft to sell!
He clashes the basins like a bell;
Tea trays, baskets ranged in order,
Plates, with alphabets round the border!

The roads are brown, and the sea is green,
But his house is like a bathing machine.
The world is round, and he can ride,
Rumble, and slash, to the other side!

With the peddler-man I should like to roam,
And write a book when I came home:
All the people would read my book
Just like the Travels of Captain Cook!

JIM AT THE CORNER

Eleanor Farjeon

Jim was a Sailor
Who sailed on the sea.
Now he sits at the corner
From breakfast to tea,
With a nod and a twinkle
For you and for me.

His hair is quite silver,
His eyes are quite blue,
His legs have got pains
So he's nothing to do
But to nod and to twinkle
At me and at you.

He tells all the weather
Without any fuss,
When he says it is thus
Then of *course* it is thus;
He nods as he says it
And twinkles at us.

He knows the world over
From east to west rim,
Now he sits on his box
And the whole world knows Jim.

151

He nods to the world,
And the world nods to him.

THE COWBOY'S LIFE

James Barton Adams

The bawl of a steer,
To a cowboy's ear,
Is music of sweetest strain;
And the yelping notes
Of the gay coyotes
To him are a glad refrain.

For a kingly crown
In the noisy town
His saddle he wouldn't change;
No life so free
As the life we see
Way out on the Yaso range.

The rapid beat
Of his broncho's feet
On the sod as he speeds along,
Keeps living time
To the ringing rhyme
Of his rollicking cowboy song.

The winds may blow
And the thunder growl
Or the breezes may safely moan; —
A cowboy's life
Is a royal life,
His saddle his kingly throne.

TEN LITTLE INDIAN BOYS

M. M. Hutchinson

One little Indian boy making a canoe,
Another came to help him and then there were two.

Two little Indian boys climbing up a tree,
They spied another one and then there were three.

Three little Indian boys playing on the shore,
They called another one and then there were four.

Four little Indian boys learning how to dive,
An older one taught them and then there were five.

Five making arrows then from slender shining sticks,
One came to lend a bow and then there were six.

Six little Indian boys wishing for eleven,
One only could they find and then there were seven.

Seven little Indian boys marched along in state,
One joined the growing line and then there were eight.

Eight little Indian boys camping near the pine,
One came with bait for fish and then there were nine.

Nine little Indian boys growing to be men,
Captured another brave and then there were ten.

TEXAS TRAINS AND TRAILS

Mary Austin

Whenever I ride on the Texas plains
I never hear the couplings cluck,
I never hear the trains
Go chuck-a-luck, chuck-a-luck, chuck-a-luck,
I never hear the engine snort and snuffle,
I never see the smoke plume, I never watch the rails,
But I see the moving dust where the beef herds shuffle,
And I think I'm a cowboy,
A rope and tie 'em cowboy,
Punching Texas longhorns
On the Texas trails.

And the engine goes *Whoop!*
Whoopee, whoopala!
And the cars go *Ki-yi,*
Ki-yi, ki-yi, coma-la ky-yi,
                    Whoopala,
Ki-yi!
                    Whoop!

No, I never hear the bell, nor the brakeman call
When I ride on the Texas trains;
But I hear the steers bellow and the yearlings bawl,
And the lone wolf howl on the wire grass plains.
And I never play I'm fireman, nor anything like that,
For I'm playing I'm a cowboy,
A bronco-bustin' cowboy,
Riding Texas longhorns
In a ten-gallon hat.

And the trains go *Youpi-ya,*
Get a-long, dogies,
Get a-long, Get a-long
Youpi-yi, youpi-ya
Youpi-youpi-youpi-ya,
Get a-long, get a-long,
Youpi-ya,
                    Yo-o-u-u-p!

THE ORGAN GRINDERS' GARDEN

Mildred Plew Merryman

In the winter, in the winter,
　　When the clouds shake snow,
I know a little garden
　　Where the organ grinders go;

A cozy little garden
　　Where the fountain makes a fizz,
And round about the lattices
　　The sunbeams sizz;

Where underneath the bushes
　　In the nodding afternoons,
The frisky little organs sit
　　And spill their tinky tunes;

While tingle, tingle, tangle,
　　Go the pennies in the cup,
As all the baby monkeys
　　Practice picking pennies up.

In the winter, in the winter,
　　When the sharp winds blow,
I know a little garden
　　Where the organ grinders go;

A giddy little garden
  Where the fruit is always ripe,
And every grinding grinder
  Sits and pulls upon a pipe;

While all the father monkeys
  Hang their fezzes on the twigs,
And teach the baby monkeys
  How to master little jigs;

Until at last the mothers come,
  As day begins to fade,
And tuck the baby monkeys up
  To snoozle in the shade.

In the winter, in the winter,
  When the clouds shake snow,
I know a little garden
  Where the organ grinders go;

A garden where the grinders
  And the monkeys on a string,
Are pleased to wait serenely
  For the coming of the spring.

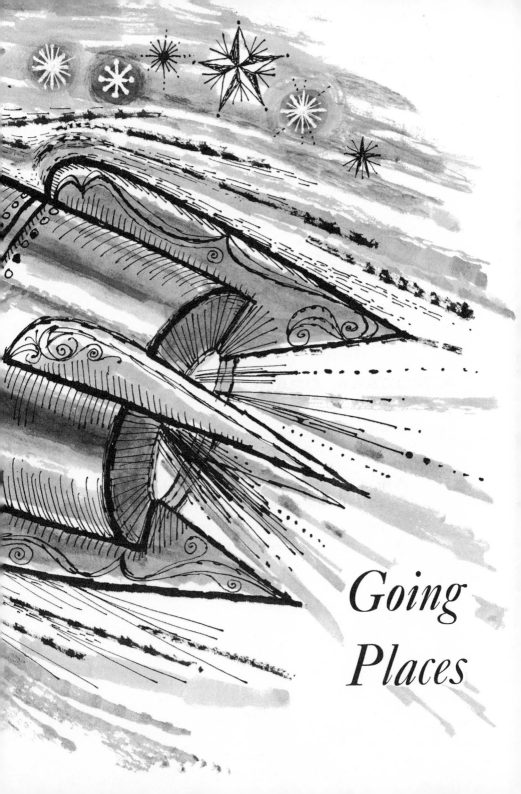

Going
Places

BRIDGES

Rhoda W. Bacmeister

I like to look for bridges
Everywhere I go,
Where the cars go over
With water down below.

Standing by the railings
I watch the water slide
Smoothly under to the dark,
And out the other side.

A MODERN DRAGON

Rowena Bennett

A train is a dragon that roars through the dark.
He wriggles his tail as he sends up a spark.
He pierces the night with his one yellow eye,
And all the earth trembles when he rushes by.

THERE ARE SO MANY WAYS OF GOING PLACES

Leslie Thompson

Big yellow trolley lumbers along,
Long black subway sings an under song,
Airplanes swoop and flash in the sky,
Noisy old elevated goes rocketing by.
Boats across the water — back and forth they go,
Big boats and little boats, fast boats and slow.
Trains puff and thunder; their engines have a headlight;
They have a special kind of car where you can sleep all night.
Tall fat buses on the Avenue,
They will stop for anyone — even — just — you.
All kinds of autos rush down the street.
And then there are always — your own two feet.

JOHNNY FIFE AND JOHNNY'S WIFE

Mildred Plew Merryman

Oh, Johnny Fife and Johnny's wife,
  To save their toes and heels,
They built themselves a little house
  That ran on rolling wheels.

They hung their parrot at the door
  Upon a painted ring,

And round and round the world they went
  And never missed a thing;

And when they wished to eat they ate,
  And after they had fed,
They crawled beneath a crazy quilt
  And gayly went to bed;

And what they cared to keep they kept,
  And what they both did not,
They poked beneath a picket fence
  And quietly forgot.

Oh, Johnny Fife and Johnny's wife,
  They took their brush and comb,
And round and round the world they went
  And also stayed at home.

B'S THE BUS

Phyllis McGinley

        B's the Bus
        The bouncing Bus,
          That bears a shopper store-ward.
        It's fun to sit
        In back of it

But seats are better forward.
Although it's big as buildings are
And looks both bold and grand,
It has to stop obligingly
If you but raise your hand.

MOTOR CARS

Rowena Bennett

From a city window, 'way up high,
I like to watch the cars go by.
They look like burnished beetles, black,
That leave a little muddy track
Behind them as they slowly crawl.
Sometimes they do not move at all
But huddle close with hum and drone
As though they feared to be alone.
They grope their way through fog and night
With the golden feelers of their light.

TAXIS

Rachel Field

Ho, for taxis green or blue,
    Hi, for taxis red,
They roll along the Avenue
    Like spools of colored thread!
        Jack-o'-Lantern yellow,
        Orange as the moon,
        Greener than the greenest grass
        Ever grew in June.
        Gaily striped or checked in squares,
        Wheels that twinkle bright,
        Don't you think that taxis make
        A very pleasant sight?
        Taxis shiny in the rain,
        Scudding through the snow,
        Taxis flashing back the sun
        Waiting in a row.
Ho, for taxis red and green,
    Hi, for taxis blue,
I wouldn't be a private car
    In sober black, would you?

CITY STREETS AND COUNTRY ROADS

Eleanor Farjeon

The city has streets —
　But the country has roads.
In the country one meets
　Blue carts with their loads
Of sweet-smelling hay,
　And mangolds, and grain:
Oh, take me away
　To the country again!

In the city one sees,
　Big trams rattle by,
And the breath of the chimneys
　That blot out the sky,
And all down the pavements
　Stiff lamp-posts one sees —
But the country has hedgerows,
　The country has trees.

As sweet as the sun
　In the country is rain:
Oh, take me away
　To the country again!

ROADS

Rachel Field

A road might lead to anywhere —
  To harbor towns and quays,
Or to a witch's pointed house
  Hidden by bristly trees.
It might lead past the tailor's door,
  Where he sews with needle and thread,
Or by Miss Pim the milliner's,
  With her hats for every head.
It might be a road to a great, dark cave
  With treasures and gold piled high,
Or a road with a mountain tied to its end,
  Blue-humped against the sky.
Oh, a road might lead you anywhere —
  To Mexico or Maine.
But then, it might just fool you, and —
  Lead you back home again!

SONG OF THE TRAIN

David McCord

Clickety-clack,
Wheels on the track,
This is the way
They begin the attack:

166

Click-ety-clack,
Click-ety-clack,
Click-ety, *clack*-ety,
Click-ety
Clack.

Clickety-clack,
Over the crack,
Faster and faster
The song of the track:
Clickety-clack,
Clickety-clack,
Clickety, clackety,
Clackety
Clack.

Riding in front,
Riding in back,
Everyone hears
The song of the track:
Clickety-clack,
Clickety-clack,
Clickety, *clickety*,
Clackety
Clack.

WINGS AND WHEELS

Nancy Byrd Turner

> Ahoy and ahoy, birds!
> We cannot have wings
> And feathers and things,
> But dashing on wheels
> With the wind at our heels
> Is almost like flying —
> Such joy, birds!
>
> Oho and oho, birds!
> Of course we can't rise
> Up and up to the skies;
> But skimming and sliding
> On rollers, and gliding,
> Is almost as jolly,
> You know, birds!

PASSENGER TRAIN

Edith Newlin Chase

When you ride on a train, a passenger train,
You walk down a long, long aisle,
With seats and seats and seats and seats
Along each side of the aisle.
You choose a seat that you like the best
And look out a window to East or West.
The train begins to move along,
The wheels begin to make a song
Speeding along on the long, long track —
Clicket-a-clacket, a-clacket, a-clack
    Go the wheels of the passenger train.

When you ride on a train, a passenger train,
You sit on a high straight seat,
You look to see if this is a train
With a sort-of-a-shelf for your feet.
You put your feet on this sort-of-a-shelf
And you settle back to enjoy yourself.
And trees fly by, and the telegraph poles
The woods and fields, the valleys and knolls,
As you rush along the long, long track,
And their wheels sing their clickety clack,
    When you ride on a passenger train.

When you ride on a train, a passenger train,
You suddenly come to a town,
And a house and a house and a house and a house
Slip by as you're slowing down.
And the passenger station comes in sight,
The train stands still while you alight,
Then it disappears down its long, long track,
With its wheels still singing the clickety-clack
    Of a hurrying passenger train.

THE WAYS OF TRAINS

Elizabeth Coatsworth

    I hear the engine pounding
    in triumph down the track —
    trains take away the ones you love
    and then they bring them back!

    Trains take away the ones you love
    to worlds both strange and new
    and then, with care and courtesy,
    they bring them back to you.

    The engine halts and snuffs and snorts,
    it breathes forth smoke and fire,
    then snatches crowded strangers on —
    but leaves what you desire!

TRAINS

James S. Tippett

Over the mountains,
Over the plains,
Over the rivers,
Here come the trains.

Carrying passengers,
Carrying mail,
Bringing their precious loads
In without fail.

Thousands of freight cars
All rushing on
Through day and darkness,
Through dusk and dawn.

Over the mountains,
Over the plains,
Over the rivers,
Here come the trains.

ENGINE

James S. Tippett

I wonder if the engine
That dashes down the track
Ever has a single thought
Of how it can get back.

With fifty cars behind it
And each car loaded full,
I wonder if it ever thinks
How hard it has to pull.

I guess it trusts the fireman;
It trusts the engineer;
I guess it knows the switchman
Will keep the tracks clear.

THE DIRIGIBLE

Ralph W. Bergengren

The only real airship
That I've ever seen
Looked more like a fish
Than a flying machine.

It made me feel funny,
And just as if we
Were all of us down
On the floor of the sea.

A big whale above us
Was taking a swim,
And we little fishes
Were staring at him.

UP IN THE AIR

James S. Tippett

Zooming across the sky,
Like a great bird you fly,
Airplane,
Silvery white
In the light.

173

Turning and twisting in air,
When shall I ever be there,
　　Airplane,
　　Piloting you
　　Far in the blue?

AEROPLANE

Mary McBride Green

There's a humming in the sky
There's a shining in the sky
Silver wings are flashing by
Silver wings are shining by
Aeroplane
Aeroplane
Flying — high.

Silver wings are shining
As it goes gliding by
First it zooms
And it booms
Then it buzzes in the sky
Then its song is just a drumming
A soft little humming
Strumming
Strumming.

The wings are very little things
The silver shine is gone

Just a little black speck
Away down the sky
With a soft little strumming
And a far-away humming
Aeroplane
Aeroplane
Gone — by.

TAKING OFF

Unknown

The airplane taxis down the field
And heads into the breeze,
It lifts its wheels above the ground,
It skims above the trees,
It rises high and higher
Away up toward the sun,
It's just a speck against the sky
— And now it's gone!

THE OLD AND THE NEW

Q. B. M.

Railroad tracks; the flight
of a rocket high above
in the starlit night.

LITTLE SATELLITE

Jane W. Krows

Once a little satellite
Reached a most unheard of height.
Far in space it soared and soared
Around the moon it roared and roared.

Like a spinning, whirling base
Orbiting around in space
Beeping, beeping all its worth
Messages sent back to earth.

What a trip for one so small
Little satellital ball.
Do you wish for earth again
When you're whirling in your spin?

Will you solve the mystery soon
Of outer space and of the moon?
I would only soar from sight
If I could return each night.

SPACE TRAVEL

Jane W. Krows

It's all aboard for outer space
Straight up from my home town
I'll board the rocket going up
And hope it will come down.

I'll bet when there, the sun will rise
Just as I go to bed
And it will set when I get up,
Not as it should, instead.

And will I know when weather's wet
And know when it is dry?
Can it rain up, as well as down,
When you are up that high?

I only have a few requests
Of Spacemen up on Mars.
May I roll out the morning sun
And hang the evening stars?

And may I hail a floating cloud
And ride it for a day?
And could I have a motel room
Along the Milky Way?

177

Will outerspace be better still
Than here, where I live now?
Will I find things I like to eat,
And can I play — and how?

If you can find the answer
To my queries very soon,
Then make my reservation
On a rocket to the moon.

FERRY-BOATS

James S. Tippett

Over the river,
Over the bay,
Ferry-boats travel
Every day.

Most of the people
Crowd to the side
Just to enjoy
Their ferry-boat ride.

Watching the seagulls,
Laughing with friends,
I'm always sorry
When the ride ends.

I'D LIKE TO BE A LIGHTHOUSE

Rachel Field

I'd like to be a lighthouse
    All scrubbed and painted white.
I'd like to be a lighthouse
    And stay awake all night
To keep my eye on everything
    That sails my patch of sea;
I'd like to be a lighthouse
    With the ships all watching me.

SHIPS

Nancy Byrd Turner

Go out, good ships, across the tide,
Be brave to meet all weathers;
Make many a port, and fill each hold
With sky-blue silk and yellow gold
And pearls and peacock feathers.

The wind is in your shining sails,
Your keen prows cut the foam;
Sail very fast and very far,
Then turn, and by the Northern Star
Come steering safely home.

BOATS

Rowena Bennett

The steamboat is a slow poke,
   You simply cannot rush him.
The sailboat will not move at all
   Without a wind to push him;

But the speed boat, with his sharp red nose,
   Is quite a different kind;
He tosses high the spray and leaves
   The other boats behind.

THE FERRYMAN

Christina Rossetti

'Ferry me across the water,
   Do, boatman, do.'
'If you've a penny in your purse
   I'll ferry you.'

'I have a penny in my purse,
    And my eyes are blue;
So ferry me across the water,
    Do, boatman, do.'

'Step into my ferry-boat,
    Be they black or blue,
And for the penny in your purse
    I'll ferry you.'

THE OLD WHARVES

Rachel Field

I'm sorry for the old wharves
    Because they have to stand
With the sea all round their wooden knees
    And never run to land
If they grow tired. They have to stay
In their places night and day.

Tilted backwards, gray and worn
    From salty tides that flow
Dark green at high-water mark,
    Weedy-brown at low —
It never stops surprising me
How they can stand so patiently!

Kick
A
Little
Stone

THE SECRET SITS

Robert Frost

We dance round in a
ring and suppose,

But the Secret sits in the
middle and knows.

THE WORLD'S SO BIG

Aileen Fisher

Think of all the people
I'll never get to know
Because the world's so big
And my wagon's so slow.

Think of all the places
I'll never get to see
Because the street's so long
And Mother's calling me!

KICK A LITTLE STONE

Dorothy Aldis

When you are walking by yourself
Here's something nice to do:
Kick a little stone and watch it
Hop ahead of you.

The little stone is round and white,
Its shadow round and blue.
Along the sidewalk over the cracks
The shadow bounces too.

I HAVE TO HAVE IT

Dorothy Aldis

I need a little stick when I
Go walking up the street,
To poke in cracks as I go by
Or point at birds up in the sky
Or whack at trees we meet.

I need a stick to zim along
The fences that we pass;
I need a stick for dragging through
The gravel or the grass.

My father says there cannot be
A single doubt about it:
I have to have a stick with me.
I cannot walk without it.

THE LESSON

Jane W. Krows

I splash — I flop,
I tread — I hop,
My arms go in a spin
My legs are kicking up and down
Then — suddenly! I swim.

SOMERSAULT

Dorothy Aldis

I somersault just like a clown
And all the trees turn upside down.

The sky is not the sky at all —
It changes to a high blue wall

And every little buttercup
Looks down at me instead of up.

THIS IS MY ROCK

David McCord

This is my rock,
And here I run
To steal the secret of the sun;

This is my rock,
And here come I
Before the night has swept the sky;

This is my rock,
This is the place
I meet the evening face to face.

MUD

Polly Chase Boyden

Mud is very nice to feel
All squishy-squash between the toes!
I'd rather wade in wiggly mud
Than smell a yellow rose.

Nobody else but the rosebush knows
How nice mud feels
Between the toes.

WHAT THEY ARE FOR

Dorothy Aldis

Curbstones are to balance on
Far from the ground.
Railings are to slide upon
And trees for running round.

Fences are for wriggling through,
Cracks and holes to hop,
And, though she does not like us to,
Puddles are to plop.

SHADOW DANCE

Ivy O. Eastwick

O Shadow,
Dear Shadow,
Come, Shadow,
And dance!
On the wall
In the firelight
Let both of
Us prance!
I raise my
Arms, thus!
And you raise

188

Your arms, so!
And dancing
And leaping
And laughing
We go!
From the wall
To the ceiling,
From ceiling
To wall,
Just you and
I, Shadow,
And none else
At all.

MY SHADOW

Robert Louis Stevenson

I have a little shadow that goes in and out with me,
And what can be the use of him is more than I can see.
He is very, very like me from the heels up to the head;
And I see him jump before me, when I jump into my bed.

The funniest thing about him is the way he likes to grow —
Not at all like proper children, which is always very slow;
For he sometimes shoots up taller like an India-rubber ball,
And he sometimes gets so little that there's none of him at all.

He hasn't got a notion of how children ought to play,
And can only make a fool of me in every sort of way.
He stays so close beside me, he's a coward you can see;
I'd think shame to stick to nursie as that shadow sticks to me!

One morning, very early, before the sun was up,
I rose and found the shining dew on every buttercup;
But my lazy little shadow, like an arrant sleepyhead,
Had stayed at home behind me and was fast asleep in bed.

THE LITTLE WHISTLER

Frances Frost

My mother whistled softly,
My father whistled bravely,
My brother whistled merrily,
And I tried all day long!
I blew my breath inwards,
I blew my breath outwards,
But all you heard was breath blowing
And not a bit of song!

But today I heard a bluebird,
A happy, young, and new bird,

Whistling in the apple tree —
He'd just discovered how!
Then quick I blew my breath in,
And gay I blew my breath out,
And sudden I blew three wild notes —
And I can whistle now!

MY BROTHER

Dorothy Aldis

My brother is inside the sheet
That gave that awful shout.
I know because those are his feet
So brown and sticking out.

And that's his head that waggles there
And his eyes peeking through —
So I can laugh, so I don't care:
"Ha!" I say. "It's you."

EVERY TIME I CLIMB A TREE

David McCord

Every time I climb a tree
Every time I climb a tree
Every time I climb a tree
I scrape a leg
Or skin a knee
And every time I climb a tree
I find some ants
Or dodge a bee
And get the ants
All over me

And every time I climb a tree
Where have you been?
They say to me
But don't they know that I am free
Every time I climb a tree?
I like it best
To spot a nest
That has an egg
Or maybe three

And then I skin
The other leg
But every time I climb a tree
I see a lot of things to see
Swallows rooftops and TV
And all the fields and farms there be
Every time I climb a tree
Though climbing may be good for ants
It isn't awfully good for pants
But still it's pretty good for me
Every time I climb a tree.

BOUNCING BALL

Sara Ruth Watson

I wish I had a great big ball
To bounce up to the sky;
I'd bounce it 'til it hit a cloud
That the wind was blowing by.

My ball would strike the cloud so hard
That it would burst in two,
And empty all its store of rain
On me, our house, and you.

HOW TO TELL THE TOP OF A HILL

John Ciardi

The top of a hill
Is not until
The bottom is below.
And you have to stop
When you reach the top
For there's no more UP to go.

To make it plain
Let me explain:
The one most reason why
You have to stop
When you reach the top — is:
The next step up is sky.

SKATING

Herbert Asquith

When I try to skate,
My feet are so wary
They grit and they grate:
And then I watch Mary

Easily gliding,
Like an ice-fairy;
Skimming and curving,
Out and in,
With a turn of her head,
And a lift of her chin,
And a gleam of her eye,
And a twirl and a spin;
Sailing under
The breathless hush
Of the willows, and back
To the frozen rush;
Out to the island
And round the edge,
Skirting the rim
Of the crackling sedge,
Swerving close
To the poplar root,
And round the lake
On a single foot,
With a three, and an eight,
And a loop and a ring;
Where Mary glides,
The lake will sing!
Out in the mist
I hear her now
Under the frost
Of the willow-bough
Easily sailing,
Light and fleet,
With the song of the lake
Beneath her feet.

A KITE

Unknown

I often sit and wish that I
Could be a kite up in the sky,
And ride upon the breeze and go
Whichever way I chanced to blow.

THE SWING

Robert Louis Stevenson

How do you like to go up in a swing,
 Up in the air so blue?
Oh, I do think it the pleasantest thing
 Ever a child can do!

Up in the air and over the wall,
 Till I can see so wide,
Rivers and trees and cattle and all
 Over the countryside —

Till I look down on the garden green,
 Down on the roof so brown —
Up in the air I go flying again,
 Up in the air and down!

THE GOLD-TINTED DRAGON

Karla Kuskin

What's the good of a wagon
Without any dragon
To pull you for mile after mile?
An elegant lean one
A gold-tinted green one
Wearing a dragonly smile.
You'll sweep down the valleys
You'll sail up the hills
Your dragon will shine in the sun
And as you rush by
The people will cry
"I wish that my wagon had one!"

THE LITTLE RED SLED

Jocelyn Bush

"Come out with me!" cried the little red sled.
"I'll give you the wings of a bird," it said.
"The ground is all snowy;
The wind is all blowy!
We'll go like a fairy,
So light and so airy!"

MERRY-GO-ROUND

Dorothy Baruch

I climbed up on the merry-go-round,
And it went round and round.

I climbed up on a big brown horse
And it went up and down.

Around and round
And up and down,
Around and round
And up and down.
I sat high up
On a big brown horse
And rode around
On the merry-go-round
And rode around

On the merry-go-round
I rode around
On the merry-go-round
Around
And round
And
Round.

HIDING

Dorothy Aldis

I'm hiding, I'm hiding,
And no one knows where;
For all they can see is my
Toes and my hair.

And I just heard my father
Say to my Mother —
"But, darling, he must be
Somewhere or other;

Have you looked in the inkwell?"
And Mother said, "Where?"
"In the inkwell," said Father. But
I was not there.

Then "Wait!" cried my Mother —
"I think that I see
Him under the carpet." But
It was not me.

"Inside the mirror's
A pretty good place,"
Said Father and looked, but saw
Only his face.

"We've hunted," sighed Mother,
"As hard as we could
And I'm so afraid that we've
Lost him for good."

Then I laughed out aloud
And I wiggled my toes
And Father said — "Look, dear,
I wonder if those

Toes could be Benny's.
There are ten of them. See?"
And they were so surprised to find
Out it was me!

THE RIVER IS A PIECE OF SKY

John Ciardi

From the top of a bridge
The river below
Is a piece of sky —
        Until you throw
        A penny in
        Or a cockleshell
        Or a pebble or two
        Or a bicycle bell
        Or a cobblestone

200

Or a fat man's cane —
And then you can see
It's a river again.

The difference you'll see
When you drop your penny:
The river has splashes,
The sky hasn't any.

WHERE GO THE BOATS?

Robert Louis Stevenson

Dark brown is the river,
    Golden is the sand.
It flows along forever,
    With trees on either hand.

Green leaves a-floating,
    Castles of the foam,
Boats of mine a-boating —
    Where will all come home?

On goes the river
    And out past the mill,
Away down the valley,
    Away down the hill.

Away down the river,
   A hundred miles or more,
Other little children
   Shall bring my boats ashore.

DOLL SONG

Lewis Carroll

Matilda Jane, you never look
At any toy or picture-book:
I show you pretty things in vain —
You must be blind, Matilda Jane;

I ask you riddles, tell you tales,
But *all* our conversation fails:
You *never* answer me again—
I fear you're dumb, Matilda Jane;

Matilda, darling, when I call,
You never seem to hear at all:
I shout with all my might and main —
But you're *so* deaf, Matilda Jane!

Matilda Jane, you needn't mind:
For though you're deaf, and dumb, and blind,
There's *someone* loves you, it is plain—
And that is *me*, Matilda Jane!

BUT THAT WAS YESTERDAY

Aileen Fisher

I was going to make a boat
and paint it green and gray.
I was going to make it float . . .
but that was yesterday,
and my knife was in my coat
and my coat was put away,
so I didn't make a boat,
and now . . . it is today.

And so I guess I'll go and borrow
Johnny's boat until tomorrow.

THE LOST DOLL

Charles Kingsley

I once had a sweet little doll, dears,
    The prettiest doll in the world;
Her cheeks were so red and so white, dears,
    And her hair was so charmingly curled.
But I lost my poor little doll, dears,
    As I played on the heath one day;
And I cried for her more than a week, dears,
    But I never could find where she lay.

203

I found my poor little doll, dears,
  As I played on the heath one day;
Folks say she is terribly changed, dears,
  For her paint is all washed away,
And her arm trodden off by the cows, dears,
  And her hair not the least bit curled;
Yet for old time's sake, she is still, dears,
  The prettiest doll in the world.

I'M THE POLICE COP MAN, I AM

Margaret Morrison

I'm the police cop man, I am, I am.
Cars can't go till I say they can.
I stand in the middle of the street, I do
And tell them to go when I want them to.
Whizzing taxis and automobiles,
Trotting horses and clattering wheels,
And rumbling, grumbling, huge big trucks
And even the lazy old trolley car
Can't go very far
            When up goes my hand
                    and
"Traffic stop," says the traffic cop.
Then many little children's feet
Go hippity across the street.

THE LAND OF COUNTERPANE

Robert Louis Stevenson

When I was sick and lay a-bed,
I had two pillows at my head,
And all my toys beside me lay
To keep me happy all the day.

And sometimes for an hour or so
I watched my leaden soldiers go,
With different uniforms and drills,
Among the bedclothes, through the hills;

And sometimes sent my ships in fleets
All up and down among the sheets;
Or brought my trees and houses out,
And planted cities all about.

I was the giant great and still
That sits upon the pillow-hill
And sees before him, dale and plain,
The pleasant land of counterpane.

HOUSES

Aileen Fisher

Houses are faces
(haven't you found?)
with their hats in the air,
and their necks in the ground.

Windows are noses,
windows are eyes,
and doors are the mouths
of a suitable size.

And a porch — or the place
where porches begin —
is just like a mustache
shading the chin.

MY HORSES

Jean Jaszi

My red horse has his stable
Underneath the kitchen table.
No one knows that he is there,
For he looks just like a chair.

I have another horse — white —
He can run as fast as light.
I keep him upstairs in my room.
People think he's just a broom.

Only I know who they are,
And I ride them pretty far,
North and South and every way
Every day.

RADIATOR LIONS

Dorothy Aldis

George lives in an apartment and
His mother will not let
Him keep a dog or polliwog
Or rabbit for a pet.

So he has Radiator Lions.
(The parlor is their zoo.)
They love to fight but never bite
Unless George tells them to.

But days when it is very cold
And George can't go outdoors
His parlor pets will glower
And crouch upon all fours

And roar most awful roarings.
The noise is very bad.
Up their noses water goeses —
That's what makes them mad.

But George loves Radiator Lions.
He's glad, although they're wild,
He hasn't dogs or polliwogs
Like any other child.

TIMOTHY BOON

Ivy O. Eastwick

Timothy Boon
Bought a balloon
Blue as the sky,
Round as the moon.
"Now I will try
To make it fly
Up to the moon,
Higher than high!"
Timothy said,
Nodding his head.

Timothy Boon
Sent his balloon
Up through the skies,
Up to the moon.

But a strong breeze
Stirred in the trees,
Rocked the bright moon,
Tossed the great seas,
And, with its mirth,
Shook the whole earth.

Timothy Boon,
And his balloon,
Caught by the breeze
Flew to the moon;
Up past the trees,
Over the seas,
Up to the moon —
Swift as you please! —
And, ere I forget,
They have not come down yet!

WILD BEASTS

Evaleen Stein

I will be a lion
    And you shall be a bear,
And each of us will have a den
    Beneath a nursery chair;
And you must growl and growl and growl,
    And I will roar and roar,
And then — why, then — you'll growl again,
    And I will roar some more!

GENERAL STORE

Rachel Field

Some day I'm going to have a store
With a tinkly bell hung over the door,
With real glass cases and counters wide
And drawers all spilly with things inside.
There'll be a little of everything;
Bolts of calico; balls of string;
Jars of peppermint; tins of tea;
Pots and kettles and crockery;
Seeds in packets; scissors bright;
Kegs of sugar, brown and white;
Sarsaparilla for picnic lunches,
Bananas and rubber boots in bunches.
I'll fix the window and dust each shelf,
And take the money in all myself,
It will be my store and I will say:
"What can I do for you to-day?"

BLOCK CITY

Robert Louis Stevenson

What are you able to build with your blocks?
Castles and palaces, temples and docks.
Rain may keep raining, and others go roam,
But I can be happy and building at home.

Let the sofa be mountains, the carpet be sea,
There I'll establish a city for me:
A kirk and a mill and a palace beside,
And a harbor as well where my vessels may ride.

Great is the palace with pillar and wall,
A sort of a tower on the top of it all,
And steps coming down in an orderly way
To where my toy vessels lie safe in the bay.

This one is sailing and that one is moored:
Hark to the song of the sailors on board!
And see on the steps of my palace, the kings
Coming and going with presents and things!

Now I have done with it, down let it go!
All in a moment the town is laid low.
Block upon block lying scattered and free,
What is there left of my town by the sea?

Yet as I saw it, I see it again,
The kirk and the palace, the ships and the men,
And as long as I live and where'er I may be,
I'll always remember my town by the sea.

FOLLOW THE LEADER

Harry Behn

Follow the leader away in a row,
Into the barn and out we go,
A long slide down the hay,
Splash in a puddle, through a hedge,
And slowly up to the buzzing edge
Of a bees' hive, then run away!
Oh what a wonderful game to play!

Follow the leader on and on,
Around a tree, across a lawn,
Under the sprinkler's drifting spray,
Eat one berry, let two drop,
A somersault and a hippity-hop!
Oh what a wonderful game to play
All over the farm on a summer day!

BEING GYPSY

Barbara Young

A gypsy, a gypsy,
Is what I'd like to be,
If ever I could find one who
Would change his place with me.

212

Rings on my fingers,
Earrings in my ears,
Rough shoes to roam the world
For years and years and years!

I'd listen to the stars,
I'd listen to the dawn,
I'd learn the tunes of wind and rain,
The talk of fox and faun.

A gypsy, a gypsy!
To ramble and to roam
For maybe — oh,
A week or so —
And then I'd hie me home!

THE LITTLE LAND

Robert Louis Stevenson

When at home alone I sit
And am very tired of it,
  I have just to shut my eyes
  To go sailing through the skies —

To go sailing far away
To the pleasant Land of Play;

To the fairy land afar
Where the little people are,
Where the clover tops are trees,
And the rain-pools are the seas.
And the leaves like little ships
Sail about on tiny trips;
And about the daisy tree
Through the grasses
High o'erhead the bumblebee
Hums and passes.

In that forest to and fro
I can wander, I can go;
See the spider and the fly,
And the ants go marching by,
Carrying parcels with their feet,
Down the green and grassy street.
I can in the sorrel sit
Where the ladybirds have lit;
I can climb the jointed grass,
And on high
See the greater swallows pass
In the sky!
And the round sun rolling by,
Heeding no such things as I.

Through the forest I can pass
Till, as in a looking-glass,
Humming fly and daisy tree
And my tiny self I see,
Painted very clear and neat

On the rain-pool at my feet.
    Should a leaflet come to land,
    Drifting near to where I stand,
Straight I'll board the tiny boat
Round the rain-pool sea to float.
    Little thoughtful creatures sit
    On the grassy coasts of it;

Little things with lovely eyes
See me sailing with surprise.
    Some are clad in armor green —
    These have sure to battle been! —
Some are pied with ev'ry hue,
Black and crimson, gold and blue;
    Some have wings and swift are gone;
    But they all look kindly on.

When my eyes I once again
Open, and see all things plain;
    High bare walls, great bare floor;
Great big knobs on drawer and door;
Great big people perched on chairs,
Stitching tucks and mending tears,
    Each a hill that I could climb,
    And talking nonsense all the time —
    O dear me!
    That I could be
A sailor on the rain-pool sea,
A climber in the clover tree,
    And just come back, a sleepy head,
    Late at night to go to bed.

Nimble
Nonsense

LAUGHING SONG

William Blake

Come live and be merry,
    and join with me,
To sing the sweet chorus
    of "Ha, ha, he!"

THE FUNNY OLD MAN AND HIS WIFE

Unknown

Once upon a time, in a little wee house,
    Lived a funny old man and his wife;
And he said something funny to make her laugh,
    Every day of his life.

One day he said such a very funny thing,
    That she shook and scream'd with laughter;
But the poor old soul, she couldn't leave off
    For at least three whole days after.

So laughing with all her might and main,
    Three days and nights she sat;
And at the end she didn't know a bit
    What she'd been laughing at.

THE MAN IN THE MOON

Mother Goose

The Man in the Moon
As he sails in the sky
Is a very remarkable skipper.
But he made a mistake
When he tried to take
A drink of milk from the Dipper.
He dipped right into the Milky Way
And slowly and carefully filled it.
The Big Bear growled
And the Little Bear howled,
And frightened him so he spilled it.

IF ALL THE WORLD WAS APPLE PIE

Unknown

If all the world was apple pie,
    And all the sea was ink,
And all the trees were bread and cheese,
    What should we have for drink?

IF ALL THE SEAS WERE ONE SEA

Unknown

If all the seas were one sea,
What a *great* sea that would be!
And if all the trees were one tree,
What a *great* tree that would be!
And if all the axes were one axe,
What a *great* axe that would be!
And if all the men were one man,
What a *great* man he would be!
And if the *great* man took the *great* axe,
And cut down the *great* tree,
And let.it fall into the *great* sea,
What a splish splash *that* would be!

THE LOLLYPOPS

Cordia Thomas

There was a great commotion
On the counter in the shop;
The lollypops got angry,
And they all began to pop.

They popped upon the counter,
   And they popped upon the floor;
They popped right out the window,
   And they popped right out the door.

And everybody ran away,
   As fast as he could go.
For who would want a lollypop
   To chase one, don't you know?

THE TABLE AND THE CHAIR

Edward Lear

Said the Table to the Chair,
"You can hardly be aware
How I suffer from the heat
And from chilblains on my feet.
If we took a little walk,
We might have a little talk;
Pray let us take the air,"
Said the Table to the Chair.

Said the Chair unto the Table,
"Now, you know we are not able:
How foolishly you talk,
When you know we cannot walk!"
Said the Table with a sigh,

"It can do no harm to try.
I've as many legs as you;
Why can't we walk on two?"

So they both went slowly down,
And walked about the town
With a cheerful bumpy sound
As they toddled round and round;
And everybody cried,
As they hastened to their side,
"See! the Table and the Chair
Have come out to take the air!"

But in going down an alley
To a castle in a valley,
They completely lost their way,
And wandered all the day;
Till, to see them safely back,
They paid a Ducky-quack,
And a Beetle, and a Mouse,
Who took them to their house.

Then they whispered to each other,
"O delightful little brother,
What a lovely walk we've taken!
Let us dine on beans and bacon."
So the Ducky and the leetle
Browny-Mousy *and* the Beetle
Dined and danced upon their heads
Till they toddled to their beds.

JIPPY AND JIMMY

Laura E. Richards

Jippy and Jimmy were two little dogs.
They went to sail on some floating logs;
The logs rolled over, the dogs rolled in,
And they got very wet, for their clothes were thin.

Jippy and Jimmy crept out again.
They said, "The river is full of rain!"
They said, "The water is far from dry!"
Ki-hi! ki-hi! ki-*hi*-yi! ki-hi!"

Jippy and Jimmy went shivering home.
They said, "On the river no more we'll roam;
And we won't go to sail until we learn how,
Bow-wow! bow-wow! bow-*wow*-wow! bow-wow!"

OVER IN THE MEADOW

Unknown

Over in the meadow, in the sand, in the sun,
Lived an old mother turtle, and her little one.
"Dig," said the mother. "We dig," said the one;
So they dug all day in the sand in the sun.

223

Over in the meadow, where the stream runs blue,
Lived an old mother fish and her little fishes two.
"Swim," said the mother. "We swim," said the two;
So they swam all day where the stream runs blue.

Over in the meadow, in a hole in a tree,
Lived an old mother owl and her little owls three.
"Tu-whoo," said the mother. "Tu-whoo," said the three;
So they tu-whooed all day in a hole in a tree.

Over in the meadow, by the old barn door,
Lived an old mother rat and her little ratties four.
"Gnaw," said the mother. "We gnaw," said the four.
So they gnawed all day by the old barn door.

Over in the meadow, in a snug beehive,
Lived an old mother bee and her little bees five.
"Buzz," said the mother. "We buzz," said the five;
So they buzzed all day in a snug beehive.

Over in the meadow, in a nest built of sticks,
Lived an old mother crow and her little crows six.
"Caw," said the mother. "We caw," said the six;
So they cawed all day in a nest built of sticks.

Over in the meadow, where the grass grows so even,
Lived an old mother frog and her little froggies seven.
"Jump," said the mother. "We jump," said the seven;
So they jumped all day where the grass grows so even.

Over in the meadow, by the old mossy gate,
Lived an old mother lizard and her little lizards eight.
"Bask," said the mother. "We bask," said the eight;
So they basked all day by the old mossy gate.

Over in the meadow, by the old scotch pine,
Lived an old mother duck and her little ducks nine.
"Quack," said the mother. "We quack," said the nine;
So they quacked all day by the old scotch pine.

Over in the meadow, in a cozy wee den,
Lived an old mother beaver and her little beavers ten.
"Beave," said the mother. "We beave," said the ten;
So they beaved all day in a cozy wee den.

CALICO PIE

Edward Lear

Calico Pie,
The little Birds fly
Down to the calico tree,
Their wings were blue,
And they sang "Tilly-loo!"
Till away they flew —
And they never came back to me!
They never came back!
They never came back!
They never came back to me!

Calico Jam,
The little Fish swam
Over the syllabub sea,
He took off his hat,
To the Sole and the Sprat,
And the Willeby-wat —
But he never came back to me!
He never came back!
He never came back!
He never came back to me!

Calico Ban,
The little Mice ran,
To be ready in time for tea,
Flippity flup,
They drank it all up,
And danced in the cup —
But they never came back to me!
They never came back!
They never came back!
They never came back to me!

Calico Drum,
The Grasshoppers come,
The Butterfly, Beetle, and Bee,
Over the ground,
Around and round,
With a hop and a bound —
But they never came back!
They never came back!
They never came back!
They never came back to me!

THE ANSWERS

Robert Clairmont

"When did the world begin and how?"
I asked a lamb, a goat, a cow:
"What's it all about and why?"
I asked a hog as he went by:

"Where will the whole thing end and when?"
I asked a duck, a goose, a hen:

And I copied all the answers too,
A quack, a honk, an oink, a moo.

WHERE ARE YOU GOING

Eliza Lee Follen

"Where are you going, my little cat?"
"I am going to town to get me a hat."
    "What! A hat for a cat!
    A cat get a hat!
Who ever yet saw a cat with a hat?"

"Where are you going, my little kittens?"
"We are going to town to get us some mittens."
  "What! Mittens for kittens!
  Do kittens wear mittens?
Who ever yet saw kittens with mittens?"

"Where are you going, my little pig?"
"I am going to town to get me a wig."
  "What! A wig for a pig!
  A pig in a wig!
Who ever yet saw a pig in a wig?"

A FARMYARD SONG

Maria Hastings

    I had a cat and the cat pleased me,
    I fed my cat by yonder tree;
      Cat goes fiddle-i-fee.

    I had a hen and the hen pleased me,
    I fed my hen by yonder tree;
      Hen goes chimmy-chuck, chimmy-chuck,
      Cat goes fiddle-i-fee.

I had a duck and the duck pleased me,
I fed my duck by yonder tree;
  Duck goes quack, quack,
  Hen goes chimmy-chuck, chimmy-chuck,
  Cat goes fiddle-i-fee.

I had a sheep and the sheep pleased me,
I fed my sheep by yonder tree,
  Sheep goes baa, baa,
  Duck, etc.

Pig goes griffy, gruffy,

Cow goes moo, moo,

Horse goes neigh, neigh,

Dog, goes bow-wow, bow-wow.

THE PURPLE COW

Gelett Burgess

  I never saw a Purple Cow,
    I never hope to see one;
  But I can tell you, anyhow,
    I'd rather see than be one.

LITTLE PIGGY

Thomas Hood

Where are you going, you little pig?
I'm leaving my mother, I'm growing so big!
　So big, young pig!
　So young, so big!
What leaving your mother, you foolish young pig!

Where are you going, you little pig?
I've got a new spade, and I'm going to dig!
　To dig, little pig!
　A little pig dig! '
Well, I never saw a pig with a spade that could dig!

Where are you going, you little pig?
Why, I'm going to have a nice ride in a gig!
　In a gig, little pig!
　What, a pig in a gig!
Well, I never yet saw a pig in a gig!

Where are you going, you little pig?
I'm going to the barber's to buy me a wig!
　A wig, little pig!
　A pig in a wig!
Why, whoever before saw a pig in a wig!

Where are you going, you little pig?
Why, I'm going to the ball to dance a fine jig!
  A jig, little pig!
  A pig dance a jig!
Well, I never before saw a pig dance a jig!

WAY DOWN SOUTH

Unknown

Way down South where bananas grow,
A grasshopper stepped on an elephant's toe.
The elephant said, with tears in his eyes,
"Pick on somebody your own size."

A CENTIPEDE WAS HAPPY QUITE

Unknown

A centipede was happy quite,
Until a frog in fun
Said, "Pray, which leg comes after which?"
This raised her mind to such a pitch
She lay distracted in the ditch
Considering how to run.

231

ONLY MY OPINION

Monica Shannon

>Is a caterpillar ticklish?
>   Well, it's always my belief
>That he giggles, as he wiggles
>   Across a hairy leaf.

THE TICKLE RHYME

Ian Serraillier

>"Who's that tickling my back?" said the wall.
>"Me," said a small
>caterpillar. "I'm learning to crawl."

SO MANY MONKEYS

Marion Edey and Dorothy Grider

>Monkey Monkey Moo!
>Shall we buy a few?
>Yellow monkeys,
>Purple monkeys,
>Monkeys red and blue.

Be a monkey, do!
Who's a monkey, who?
He's a monkey,
She's a monkey,
You're a monkey, too!

HOW DOTH THE LITTLE CROCODILE

Lewis Carroll

How doth the little crocodile
Improve his shining tail,
And pour the waters of the Nile
On every golden scale!

How cheerfully he seems to grin,
How neatly spreads his claws,
And welcomes little fishes in,
With gently smiling jaws!

THE REASON FOR THE PELICAN

John Ciardi

The reason for the pelican
Is difficult to see:
His beak is clearly larger
Than there's any need to be.

233

It's not to bail a boat with —
He doesn't own a boat.
Yet everywhere he takes himself
He has that beak to tote.

It's not to keep his wife in —
His wife has got one, too.
It's not a scoop for eating soup.
It's not an extra shoe.

It isn't quite for anything.
And yet you realize
It's really quite a splendid beak
In quite a splendid size.

SOME FISHY NONSENSE

Laura E. Richards

Timothy Tiggs and Tomothy Toggs
They both went a-fishing for pollothywogs;
    They both went a-fishing
    Because they were wishing
To see how the creatures would turn into frogs.

Timothy Tiggs and Tomothy Toggs,
They both got stuck in the bogothybogs;
   They caught a small minnow,
   And said 't was a sin oh!
That things with no legs should pretend to be frogs.

THE FROGS' SINGING-SCHOOL

E. T. Carbell

Down in the rushes beside the pool,
The frogs were having a singing-school —
Old frogs, young frogs, tadpoles and all,
Doing their best at their leader's call.
He waved a grass blade high in the air,
And cried "Ker-chunk!" — which means "Prepare!"
But the youngest singer took up the strain
And sang "Ker-chunk!" with might and main.
The others followed as he sang.
"Ker-chunk!" their voices loudly rang,
Until their leader so angry grew
He snapped his baton quite in two
And croaked, "Oh, wrong, oh wro-ong! Oh, wro-ong!"
Which his class mistook for another song.
At that, their leader hopped away.
"Ker-chunk! Oh, wro-ong!" I heard him say.
Then flop! he went, right into the pool,
And that was the end of the singing-school.

KINDNESS TO ANIMALS

Laura E. Richards

Riddle cum diddle cum dido,
My little dog's name is Fido;
   I bought him a wagon,
   And hitched up a dragon,
And off we both went for a ride, oh!

Riddle cum diddle cum doodle,
My little cat's name is Toodle;
   I curled up her hair,
   But she only said, "There!
You have made me look *just* like a poodle!"

Riddle cum diddle cum dinky,
My little pig's name is Winkie;
   I keep him quite clean
   With the washing machine,
And I rinse him all off in the sinkie.

FURRY BEAR

A. A. Milne

If I were a bear,
   And a big bear too,

236

I shouldn't much care
　　If it froze or snew;
I shouldn't much mind
　　If it snowed or friz —
I'd be all fur-lined
　　With a coat like his!

For I'd have fur boots and a brown fur wrap,
And brown fur knickers and a big fur cap.
I'd have a fur muffle-ruff to cover my jaws.
And brown fur mittens on my big brown paws.
With a big brown furry-down up to my head,
I'd sleep all the winter in a big fur bed.

LAUGHING TIME

William Jay Smith

It was laughing time, and the tall Giraffe
Lifted his head, and began to laugh:

Ha! Ha! Ha! Ha!

And the Chimpanzee on the ginkgo tree
Swung merrily down with a Tee Hee Hee:

Hee! Hee! Hee! Hee!

"It's certainly not against the law!"
Croaked Justice Crow with a loud guffaw:

Haw! Haw! Haw! Haw!

The dancing Bear who could never say "No"
Waltzed up and down on the tip of his toe:

Ho! Ho! Ho! Ho!

The Donkey daintily took his paw,
And around they went: Hee-Haw! Hee-Haw!

Hee-Haw! Hee-Haw!

The Moon had to smile as it started to climb;
All over the world it was laughing time!

Ho! Ho! Ho! Ho! Hee-Haw! Hee-Haw!
Hee! Hee! Hee! Hee! Ha! Ha! Ha! Ha!

THE PANTHER

Ogden Nash

The panther is like a leopard,
Except it hasn't been peppered.
Should you behold a panther crouch,
Prepare to say Ouch.
Better yet, if called by a panther,
Don't anther.

THE ELEPHANT

Hilaire Belloc

When people call this beast to mind,
They marvel more and more
At such a little tail behind,
So LARGE a trunk before.

ELETELEPHONY

Laura E. Richards

Once there was an elephant,
Who tried to use the telephant —
No! no! I mean an elephone
Who tried to use the telephone —

(Dear me! I am not certain quite
That even now I've got it right.)

Howe'er it was, he got his trunk
Entangled in the telephunk;
The more he tried to get it free,
The louder buzzed the telephee —
(I fear I'd better drop the song
Of elephop and telephong!)

THERE ONCE WAS A PUFFIN

Florence Page Jaques

Oh, there once was a Puffin
Just the shape of a muffin,
And he lived on an island
In the
    bright
       blue
          sea!

He ate little fishes,
That were most delicious,
And he had them for supper
And he
    had
       them
          for tea.

But this poor little Puffin
He couldn't play nothin',
For he hadn't anybody
To
   play
      with
         at all.

So he sat on his island,
And he cried for awhile, and
He felt very lonely,
And he
   felt
      very
         small.

Then along came the fishes,
And they said, "If you wishes,
You can have us for playmates,
Instead
   of
      for
         tea!"

So they now play together,
In all sorts of weather,
And the puffin eats pancakes,
Like you
   and
      like
         me.

THE OSTRICH IS A SILLY BIRD

Mary E. Wilkins Freeman

The ostrich is a silly bird,
  With scarcely any mind.
He often runs so very fast,
  He leaves himself behind.

And when he gets there, has to stand
  And hang about till night,
Without a blessed thing to do
  Until he comes in sight.

THE CAMEL

Ogden Nash

The camel has a single hump;
The dromedary two;
Or else the other way around.
I'm never sure. Are you?

THERE WAS AN OLD MAN,
ON WHOSE NOSE

Edward Lear

There was an Old Man, on whose nose,
Most birds of the air could repose;
But they all flew away, at the closing of day,
Which relieved that Old Man and his nose.

THERE WAS AN OLD MAN
WITH A BEARD

Edward Lear

There was an old man with a beard,
Who said, "It is just as I feared! —
Two Owls and a Hen, four Larks and a Wren,
Have all built their nests in my beard!"

THERE WAS AN OLD MAN IN A TREE

Edward Lear

There was an Old Man in a tree,
Who was horribly bored by a Bee;
When they said, "Does it buzz?" he replied, "Yes, it does!"
"It's a regular brute of a Bee!"

THERE WAS A YOUNG LADY WHOSE CHIN

Edward Lear

There was a Young Lady whose chin,
Resembled the point of a pin;
So she had it made sharp, and purchased a harp,
And played several tunes with her chin.

THERE WAS A YOUNG LADY OF NIGER

Cosmo Monkhouse

There was a young lady of Niger
Who smiled as she rode on a tiger;
   They returned from the ride
   With the lady inside,
And the smile on the face of the tiger.

GREGORY GRIGGS

Laura E. Richards

Gregory Griggs, Gregory Griggs,
Had forty-seven different wigs;
He wore them up, and he wore them down,
To please the people of Boston town.
He wore them east, and he wore them west,
But he never could tell which he liked the best.

OLD QUIN QUEERIBUS

Nancy Byrd Turner

Old Quin Queeribus —
    He loved his garden so,
He wouldn't have a rake around,
    A shovel or a hoe.

For each potato's eyes he bought
    Fine spectacles of gold,
And mufflers for the corn, to keep
    Its ears from getting cold.

On every head of lettuce green —
    What do you think of that?
And every head of cabbage, too,
    He tied a garden hat.

Old Quin Queeribus —
    He loved his garden so,
He couldn't eat his growing things,
    He only let them grow!

ANTONIO

Laura E. Richards

Antonio, Antonio,
Was tired of living alonio.
   He thought he would woo
   Miss Lissamy Lu,
Miss Lissamy Lucy Molonio.

Antonio, Antonio,
Rode off on his polo-ponio.
   He found the fair maid
   In a bowery shade,
A-sitting and knitting alonio.

Antonio, Antonio,
Said, "If you will be my ownio,
   I'll love you true,
   And I'll buy for you,
An icery creamery conio!"

"Oh, nonio, Antonio!
You're far too bleak and bonio!
   And all that I wish,
   You singular fish,
Is that you will quickly begonio."

Antonio, Antonio,
He uttered a dismal moanio;
Then ran off and hid
(Or I'm told that he did)
In the Antarctical Zonio.

MRS. SNIPKIN AND
MRS. WOBBLECHIN

Laura E. Richards

Skinny Mrs. Snipkin,
With her little pipkin,
Sat by the fireside a-warming of her toes.
Fat Mrs. Wobblechin,
With her little doublechin,
Sat by the window a-cooling of her nose.

Says this one to that one,
"Oh! You silly fat one,
Will you shut the window down? You're freezing me to death!"
Says that one to t'other one,
"Good gracious, how you bother one!
There isn't air enough for me to draw my precious breath!"

Skinny Mrs. Snipkin,
Took her little pipkin,
Threw it straight across the room as hard as she could throw;
Hit Mrs. Wobblechin
On her little doublechin,
And out of the window a-tumble she did go.

THIS OLD MAN

Unknown

This old man, he played one,
He played nick nack on my drum;
Nick nack paddy whack, give a dog a bone,
This old man came rolling home.

This old man, he played two,
He played nick nack on my shoe;
Nick nack paddy whack, give a dog a bone,
This old man came rolling home.

This old man, he played three,
He played nick nack on my tree;
Nick nack paddy whack, give a dog a bone,
This old man came rolling home.

This old man, he played four,
He played nick nack on my door;
Nick nack paddy whack, give a dog a bone,
This old man came rolling home.

This old man, he played five,
He played nick nack on my hive;
Nick nack paddy whack, give a dog a bone,
This old man came rolling home.

This old man, he played six,
He played nick nack on my sticks;
Nick nack paddy whack, give a dog a bone,
This old man came rolling home.

This old man, he played seven,
He played nick nack on my Devon;
Nick nack paddy whack, give a dog a bone,
This old man came rolling home.

This old man, he played eight,
He played nick nack on my gate;
Nick nack paddy whack, give a dog a bone,
This old man came rolling home.

This old man, he played nine,
He played nick nack on my line;
Nick nack paddy whack, give a dog a bone,
This old man came rolling home.

This old man, he played ten,
He played nick nack on my hen;
Nick nack paddy whack, give a dog a bone,
This old man came rolling home.

POP GOES THE WEASEL

Unknown

A penny for a ball of thread,
Another for a needle.
That's the way the money goes;
  Pop goes the Weasel!

All around the cobbler's bench,
The monkey chased the people;
The donkey thought 'twas all in fun.
  Pop goes the Weasel!

Queen Victoria's very sick;
Napoleon's got the measles;
Sally's got the whooping cough;
  As Pop goes the Weasel!

Of all the dances ever planned,
To fling the heel and fly the hand,
There's none that moves so gay and grand
  As Pop goes the Weasel!

A penny for a ball of thread,
Another for a needle.
That's the way the money goes;
  Pop goes the Weasel!

POOR OLD LADY

Unknown

Poor old lady, she swallowed a fly,
I don't know why she swallowed a fly.
Poor old lady, I think she'll die.

Poor old lady, she swallowed a spider.
It squirmed and wriggled and turned inside her,
She swallowed the spider to catch the fly.
I don't know why she swallowed a fly.
Poor old lady, I think she'll die.

Poor old lady, she swallowed a bird.
How absurd! She swallowed a bird.
She swallowed the bird to catch the spider,
She swallowed the spider to catch the fly,
I don't know why she swallowed a fly.
Poor old lady, I think she'll die.

Poor old lady, she swallowed a cat.
Think of that! She swallowed a cat.
She swallowed the cat to catch the bird.
She swallowed the bird to catch the spider,
She swallowed the spider to catch the fly,
I don't know why she swallowed a fly.
Poor old lady, I think she'll die.

Poor old lady, she swallowed a dog.
She went the whole hog when she swallowed the dog.
She swallowed the dog to catch the cat,
She swallowed the cat to catch the bird,
She swallowed the bird to catch the spider,
She swallowed the spider to catch the fly,
I don't know why she swallowed a fly.
Poor old lady, I think she'll die.

Poor old lady, she swallowed a cow.
I don't know how she swallowed the cow.
She swallowed the cow to catch the dog,
She swallowed the dog to catch the cat,
She swallowed the cat to catch the bird,
She swallowed the bird to catch the spider,
She swallowed the spider to catch the fly,
I don't know why she swallowed a fly.
Poor old lady, I think she'll die.

Poor old lady, she swallowed a horse.
She died, of course.

A PIG TALE

James Reeves

Poor Jane Higgins,
She had five piggins,

And one got drowned in the Irish Sea.
　　Poor Jane Higgins,
　　She had four piggins,
And one flew over a sycamore tree.
　　Poor Jane Higgins,
　　She had three piggins,
And one was taken away for pork.
　　Poor Jane Higgins,
　　She had two piggins,
And one was sent to the Bishop of Cork.
　　Poor Jane Higgins,
　　She had one piggin,
And that was struck by a shower of hail,
　　So poor Jane Higgins,
　　She had no piggins,
And that's the end of my little pig tale.

WYNKEN, BLYNKEN, AND NOD

Eugene Field

Wynken, Blynken, and Nod one night
　　Sailed off in a wooden shoe —
Sailed on a river of crystal light,
　　Into a sea of dew.
"Where are you going, and what do you wish?"
　　The old moon asked the three.
"We have come to fish for the herring fish
　　That live in this beautiful sea;

Nets of silver and gold have we!"
      Said Wynken,
      Blynken,
      And Nod.

The old moon laughed and sang a song,
  As they rocked in the wooden shoe,
And the wind that sped them all night long
  Ruffled the waves of dew.
The little stars were the herring fish
  That lived in the beautiful sea —
"Now cast your nets wherever you wish —
  Never afeard are we";
  So cried the stars to the fishermen three:
      Wynken,
      Blynken,
      And Nod.

All night long their nets they threw
  To the stars in the twinkling foam —
Then down from the skies came the wooden shoe,
  Bringing the fishermen home;
'Twas all so pretty a sail it seemed
  As if it could not be,
And some folks thought 'twas a dream they'd dreamed
  Of sailing that beautiful sea —
  But I shall name you the fishermen three:
      Wynken,
      Blynken,
      And Nod.

Wynken and Blynken are two little eyes,
   And Nod is a little head,
And the wooden shoe that sailed the skies
   Is a wee one's trundle-bed.
So shut your eyes while mother sings
   Of wonderful sights that be,
And you shall see the beautiful things
   As you rock in the misty sea,
      Where the old shoe rocked the fishermen three:
         Wynken,
         Blynken,
         And Nod.

JONATHAN BING

Beatrice Curtis Brown

Poor old Jonathan Bing
Went out in his carriage to visit the King,
But everyone pointed and said, "Look at that!
Jonathan Bing has forgotten his hat!"
(He'd forgotten his hat!)

Poor old Jonathan Bing
Went home and put on a new hat for the King,
But up by the palace a soldier said, "Hi!"
You can't see the King; you've forgotten your tie!"
(He'd forgotten his tie!)

Poor old Jonathan Bing
He put on a *beautiful* tie for the King,
But when he arrived an Archbishop said, "Ho!
You can't come to court in pyjamas, you know!"

Poor old Jonathan Bing
Went home and addressed a short note to the King:
    If you please will excuse me
    I won't come to tea;
    For home's the best place for
    All people like me!

A NEW SONG TO SING ABOUT JONATHAN BING

Beatrice Curtis Brown

O Jonathan Bing, O Bingathon Jon,
Forgets where he's going and thinks he has gone.
He wears his false teeth on the top of his head,
And always stands up when he's sleeping in bed.

O Jonathan Bing has a curious way
Of trying to walk into yesterday.
"If I end with my breakfast and start with my tea,
I *ought* to be able to do it," says he.

O Jonathan Bing is a miser, they say,
For he likes to save trouble and put it away.
"If I never get up in the morning," he said,
"I shall save all the trouble of going to bed!"

"O Jonathan Bing! What a way to behave!
And what do you do with the trouble you save?"
"I wrap it up neatly and send it by post
To my friends and relations who need it the most."

TOPSY-TURVY LAND

H. E. Wilkinson

The people walk upon their heads,
    The sea is made of sand,
The children go to school by night,
    In Topsy-Turvy Land.

The front-door step is at the back,
    You're walking when you stand,
You wear your hat upon your feet,
    In Topsy-Turvy Land.

And buses on the sea you'll meet,
    While pleasure boats are planned

To travel up and down the streets
    Of Topsy-Turvy Land.

You pay for what you never get,
    I think it must be grand,
For when you go you're coming back,
    In Topsy-Turvy Land.

A NONSENSE ALPHABET

Edward Lear

A

A was once an apple-pie,
        Pidy,
        Widy,
        Tidy,
        Pidy,
    Nice insidy,
    Apple-pie!

B

B was once a little bear,
        Beary,
        Wary,
        Hairy,
        Beary,
    Taky cary,
    Little bear!

C

C was once a little cake,
        Caky,
        Baky,
        Maky,
        Caky,
    Taky caky,
    Little cake!

D

D was once a little doll,
        Dolly,
        Molly,
        Polly,
        Nolly,
    Nursy dolly,
    Little doll!

E

E was once a little eel,
        Eely,
        Weely,
        Peely,
        Eely,
    Twirly, tweely,
    Little eel!

F

F was once a little fish,
        Fishy,
        Wishy,

Squishy,
Fishy,
In a dishy,
Little fish!

G

G was once a little goose,
Goosy,
Moosy,
Boosy,
Goosy,
Waddly-woosy,
Little goose!

H

H was once a little hen
Henny,
Chenny,
Tenny,
Henny,
Eggsy-any,
Little hen!

I

I was once a bottle of ink,
Inky,
Dinky,
Thinky,
Inky,
Blacky minky,
Bottle of ink!

J

J was once a jar of jam,
Jammy,
Mammy,
Clammy,
Jammy,
Sweety, swammy,
Jar of jam!

K

K was once a little kite,
Kity,
Whity,
Flighty,
Kity,
Out of sighty,
Little kite!

L

L was once a little lark,
Larky,
Marky,
Harky,
Larky,
In the parky,
Little lark!

M

M was once a little mouse,
Mousy,

Bousy,
Sousy,
Mousy,
In the housy,
Little mouse!

N

N was once a little needle,
Needly,
Tweedly,
Threedly,
Needly,
Wiskly, wheedly,
Little needle!

O

O was once a little owl,
Owly,
Prowly,
Howly,
Owly,
Browny fowly,
Little owl!

P

P was once a little pump,
Pumpy,
Slumpy,
Flumpy,

Pumpy,
Dumpy, thumpy,
Little pump!

Q

Q was once a little quail,
Quaily,
Faily,
Daily,
Quaily,
Stumpy-taily,
Little quail!

R

R was once a little rose,
Rosy,
Posy,
Nosy,
Rosy,
Blows-y, grows-y,
Little rose!

S

S was once a shrimp,
Shrimpy,
Nimpy,
Flimpy,
Shrimpy,
Jumpy, jimpy,
Little shrimp!

T

T was once a little thrush,
Thrushy,
Hushy,
Bushy,
Thrushy,
Flitty, flushy,
Little thrush!

U

U was once a little urn,
Urny,
Burny,
Turny,
Urny,
Bubbly, burny,
Little urn!

V

V was once a little vine,
Viny,
Winy,
Twiny,
Viny,
Twisty, twiny,
Little vine!

W

W was once a whale,
Whaly,
Scaly,

Shaly,
Whaly,
Tumbly-taily,
Mighty whale!

X

X was once a great king Xerxes
Xerxy,
Perxy,
Turxy,
Xerxy,
Linxy, lurxy,
Great King Xerxes!

Y

Y was once a little yew,
Yewdy,
Fewdy,
Crudy,
Yewdy,
Growdy, grewdy,
Little yew!

Z

Z was once a piece of zinc,
Tinky,
Winky,
Blinky,
Tinky,
Tinkly, minky,
Piece of zinc!

THE OWL AND THE PUSSY-CAT

Edward Lear

The Owl and the Pussy-Cat went to sea
    In a beautiful pea-green boat,
They took some honey, and plenty of money
    Wrapped up in a five-pound note .
The Owl looked up to the stars above,
    And sang to a small guitar,
"O lovely Pussy, O Pussy, my love,
    What a beautiful Pussy you are,
            You are,
            You are!
What a beautiful Pussy you are!"

Pussy said to the Owl, "You elegant fowl!
    How charmingly sweet you sing!
Oh! let us be married, too long we have tarried:
    But what shall we do for a ring?"
They sailed away, for a year and a day,
    To the land where the Bong-tree grows;
And there in a wood a Piggy-wig stood,
    With a ring at the end of his nose,
            His nose,
            His nose,
With a ring at the end of his nose.

"Dear Pig, are you willing to sell for one shilling
    Your ring?" Said the Piggy, "I will."
So they took it away, and were married next day
    By the Turkey who lives on the hill.
They dined on mince and slices of quince,
    Which they ate wth a runcible spoon;
And hand in hand, on the edge of the sand,
    They danced by the light of the moon,
            The moon,
            The moon,
    They danced by the light of the moon.

THE JUMBLIES

Edward Lear

They went to sea in a sieve, they did;
    In a sieve they went to sea:
In spite of all their friends could say,
On a winter's morn, on a stormy day,
    In a sieve they went to sea.
And when the sieve turned round and round,
And every one cried, "You'll all be drowned!"
They called aloud, "Our sieve ain't big;
But we don't care a button, we don't care a fig:
    In a sieve we'll go to sea!"
        Far and few, far and few,
            Are the lands where the Jumblies live:
            Their heads are green, and their hands are blue;
            And they went to sea in a sieve.

They sailed away in a sieve, they did,
  In a sieve they sailed so fast,
With only a beautiful pea-green veil
Tied with a ribbon, by way of a sail,
  To a small tobacco-pipe mast.
And every one said who saw them go,
"Oh! won't they be soon upset, you know?
For the sky is dark, and the voyage is long;
And, happen what may, it's extremely wrong
  In a sieve to sail so fast."
    Far and few, far and few,
      Are the lands where the Jumblies live:
      Their heads are green, and their hands are blue;
      And they went to sea in a sieve.

The water it soon came in, it did;
  The water it soon came in:
So, to keep them dry, they wrapped their feet
In a pinky paper all folded neat;
  And they fastened it down with a pin.
And they passed the night in a crockery-jar;
And each of them said, "How wise we are!
Though the sky be dark, and the voyage be long,
Yet we never can think we were rash or wrong,
  While round in our sieve we spin."
    Far and few, far and few,
      Are the lands where the Jumblies live:
      Their heads are green, and their hands are blue;
      And they went to sea in a sieve.

268

And all night long they sailed away;
   And when the sun went down,
They whistled and warbled a moony song,
To the echoing sound of a coppery gong,
   In the shade of the mountains brown.
"O Timballoo! How happy we are
When we live in a sieve and a crockery-jar!
And all night long, in the moonlight pale,
We sail away with a pea-green sail
   In the shade of the mountains brown."
      Far and few, far and few,
         Are the lands where the Jumblies live:
         Their heads are green, and their hands are blue;
         And they went to sea in a sieve.

They sailed to the Western Sea, they did, —
   To a land all covered with trees:
And they bought an owl, and a useful cart,
And a pound of rice, and a cranberry-tart,
   And a hive of silvery bees;
And they bought a pig, and some green jackdaws,
And a lovely monkey with lollipop paws,
And forty bottles of ring-bo-ree,
   And no end of Stilton cheese,
      Far and few, far and few,
         Are the lands where the Jumblies live:
         Their heads are green, and their hands are blue;
         And they went to sea in a sieve.

And in twenty years they all came back, —
   In twenty years or more;

And every one said, "How tall they've grown!
For they've been to the Lakes, and the Torrible Zone,
    And the hills of the Chankly Bore."
And they drank their health, and gave them a feast
Of dumplings made of beautiful yeast;
And every one said, "If we only live,
We, too, will go to sea in a sieve,
    To the hills of the Chankly Bore,"
Far and few, far and few,
    Are the lands where the Jumblies live:
Their heads are green, and their hands are blue;
    And they went to sea in a sieve.

THE PIRATE DON DURK OF DOWDEE

Mildred Plew Merryman

Ho, for the Pirate Don Durk of Dowdee!
He was as wicked as wicked could be,
But oh, he was perfectly gorgeous to see!
    The Pirate Don Durk of Dowdee.

His conscience, of course, was as black as a bat,
But he had a floppety plume on his hat
And when he went walking it jiggled — like that!
    The plume of the Pirate Dowdee.

His coat it was crimson and cut with a slash,
And often as ever he twirled his mustache
Deep down in the ocean the mermaids went splash,
    Because of Don Durk of Dowdee.

Moreover, Dowdee had a purple tattoo,
And stuck in his belt where he buckled it through
Were a dagger, a dirk and a squizzamaroo,
    For fierce was the Pirate Dowdee.

So fearful he was he would shoot at a puff,
And always at sea when the weather grew rough
He drank from a bottle and wrote on his cuff,
    Did Pirate Don Durk of Dowdee.

Oh, he had a cutlass that swung at his thigh
And he had a parrot called Pepperkin Pye,
And a zigzaggy scar at the end of his eye
    Had Pirate Don Durk of Dowdee.

He kept in a cavern, this buccaneer bold,
A curious chest that was covered with mould,
And all of his pockets were jingly with gold!
    Oh jing! went the gold of Dowdee.

His conscience, of course, it was crook'd like a squash,
But both of his boots made a slickery slosh,
And he went through the world with a wonderful swash,
    Did Pirate Don Durk of Dowdee.

It's true he was wicked as wicked could be,
His sins they outnumbered a hundred and three,
But oh, he was perfectly gorgeous to see,
  The Pirate Don Durk of Dowdee.

THE MONKEYS AND THE CROCODILE

Laura E. Richards

Five little monkeys
  Swinging from a tree;
Teasing Uncle Crocodile
  Merry as can be.
Swinging high, swinging low,
  Swinging left and right:
"Dear Uncle Crocodile,
  Come and take a bite!"

Five little monkeys
  Swinging in the air;
Heads up, tails up,
  Little do they care.
Swinging up, swinging down,
  Swinging far and near:
"Poor Uncle Crocodile,
  Aren't you hungry, dear?"

Four little monkeys
Sitting in the tree;
Heads down, tails down,
Dreary as can be.
Weeping loud, weeping low,
Crying to each other:
"Wicked Uncle Crocodile,
To gobble up our brother!"

THE DUEL

Eugene Field

The gingham dog and the calico cat
Side by side on the table sat;
'Twas half past twelve, and (what do you think!)
Nor one nor t'other had slept a wink!
The old Dutch clock and the Chinese plate
Appeared to know as sure as fate
There was going to be a terrible spat.
(I wasn't there; I simply state
What was told to me by the Chinese plate!)

The gingham dog went, "Bow-wow-wow!"
And the calico cat replied "Mee-ow!"
The air was littered, an hour or so,
With bits of gingham and calico,

While the old Dutch clock in the chimney-place
Up with its hands before its face,
For it always dreaded a family row!
(*Now mind: I'm only telling you*
What the old Dutch clock declares is true!)

The Chinese plate looked very blue,
And wailed, "Oh, dear! what shall we do!"
But the gingham dog and the calico cat
Wallowed this way and tumbled that,
Employing every tooth and claw
In the awfullest way you ever saw —
And, oh! how the gingham and calico flew!
(*Don't fancy I exaggerate—*
I got my news from the Chinese plate!)

Next morning, where the two had sat
They found no trace of dog or cat;
And some folks think unto this day
That burglars stole that pair away!
But the truth about the cat and pup
Is this: they ate each other up!
Now what do you really think of that!
(*The old Dutch clock it told me so,*
And that is how I came to know.)

FROM THE BALLAD OF
TWO-GUN FREDDY

Walter R. Brooks

Up to the ranch rides cowboy Freddy;
His heart is stout and his hand is steady;
He yells: "Come out" but Flint is yeller
And he shakes and he shivers and he hides in the cellar.
    Oh, yip, yip, yippy-doodle-dee!
When Freddy finds him he falls on his knees,
And he says, "Oh, mercy!" and he says, "Oh, please!"
But Freddy just laughs and pulls his moustache,
And he plugs old Flint in the middle of his sash.
    Sing yip, yip, yippy-doodle-do.

THE WALRUS AND THE CARPENTER

Lewis Carroll

The sun was shining on the sea,
    Shining with all his might:
He did his very best to make
    The billows smooth and bright —
And this was odd, because it was
    The middle of the night.

The moon was shining sulkily,
    Because she thought the sun
Had got no business to be there
    After the day was done —
"It's very rude of him," she said,
    "To come and spoil the fun!"

The sea was wet as wet could be,
    The sands were dry as dry.
You could not see a cloud, because
    No cloud was in the sky:
No birds were flying overhead —
    There were no birds to fly.

The Walrus and the Carpenter
    Were walking close at hand:
They wept like anything to see
    Such quantities of sand.
"If this were only cleared away,"
    They said, "it *would* be grand!"

"If seven maids with seven mops
    Swept it for half a year,
Do you suppose," the Walrus said,
    "That they could get it clear?"
"I doubt it," said the Carpenter,
    And shed a bitter tear.

"O Oysters, come and walk with us!"
    The Walrus did beseech.

"A pleasant talk, a pleasant walk,
　　Along the briny beach:
We cannot do with more than four,
　　To give a hand to each."

The eldest Oyster looked at him,
　　But never a word he said:
The eldest Oyster winked his eye,
　　And shook his heavy head —
Meaning to say he did not choose
　　To leave the oyster bed.

But four young Oysters hurried up,
　　All eager for the treat:
Their coats were brushed, their faces washed,
　　Their shoes were clean and neat —
And this was odd, because, you know,
　　They hadn't any feet.

Four other Oysters followed them,
　　And yet another four;
And thick and fast they came at last,
　　And more, and more, and more —
All hopping through the frothy waves,
　　And scrambling to the shore.

The Walrus and the Carpenter
　　Walked on a mile or so,
And then they rested on a rock
　　Conveniently low:

And all the little Oysters stood
   And waited in a row.

"The time has come," the Walrus said,
   "To talk of many things:
Of shoes and ships and sealing wax,
   Of cabbages and kings;
And why the sea is boiling hot —
   And whether pigs have wings."

"But wait a bit," the Oysters cried,
   "Before we have our chat;
For some of us are out of breath,
   And all of us are fat!"
"No hurry!" said the Carpenter.
   They thanked him much for that.

"A loaf of bread," the Walrus said,
   "Is what we chiefly need:
Pepper and vinegar besides
   Are very good indeed —
Now, if you're ready, Oysters dear,
   We can begin to feed."

"But not on us!" the Oysters cried,
   Turning a little blue.
"After such kindness, that would be
   A dismal thing to do!"
"The night is fine," the Walrus said.
   "Do you admire the view?"

"It was so kind of you to come!
    And you are very nice!"
The Carpenter said nothing but
    "Cut us another slice.
I wish you were not quite so deaf —
    I've had to ask you twice!"

"It seems a shame," the Walrus said,
    "To play them such a trick,
After we've brought them out so far,
    And made them trot so quick!"
The Carpenter said nothing but
    "The butter's spread too thick!"

"I weep for you," the Walrus said:
    "I deeply sympathize."
With sobs and tears he sorted out
    Those of the largest size,
Holding his pocket handkerchief
    Before his streaming eyes.

"O Oysters," said the Carpenter,
    "You've had a pleasant run!
Shall we be trotting home again?"
    But answer came there none —
And this was scarcely odd, because
    They'd eaten every one.

THE HIGH BARBAREE

Laura E. Richards

As I was sailing down the coast
　　Of High Barbaree,
I chanced to see a Muffin Bird
　　A-sitting in a tree.

Oh, mournfully he sang,
　　And sorrowful he sat,
Because he was a-frightened of
　　The Crum-pet Cat!

The Crumpet Cat is little known;
　　He sits him under trees,
And watches for the Muffin Bird
　　His palate for to please.

And then he opens wide his mouth,
　　The cruel Crumpet Cat,
And the Muffin Bird falls into it,
　　Just—like—*that!*

I left the ship, I gained the shore,
　　And to the tree I hied,
Just as the Cat was opening
　　His jaws wide, wide!

I waved my arms and shouted loud,
  "Shoo! *Shoo!* SHOO!"
And off the Cat went flumpering,
  And off the birdie flew.

MORAL

When you sail the Barbaree,
  Mind what you're about!
Always carry with you
  A good loud shout!

When you see a Crumpet Cat,
  Let your shout be heard;
For you may save the life of
  A pretty Muffin Bird!

Wee
Folk
And
Such

THE LITTLE MAN WHO
WASN'T THERE

Hughes Mearns

As I was going up the stair
    I met a man who wasn't there!
He wasn't there again today!
    I wish, I *wish* he'd stay away!

SOME ONE

Walter de la Mare

Some one came knocking
    At my wee, small door;
Some one came knocking,
    I'm sure — sure — sure;
I listened, I opened,
    I looked to left and right,
But nought there was a-stirring
    In the still dark night;
Only the busy beetle
    Tap-tapping in the wall,
Only from the forest
    The screech-owl's call,
Only the cricket whistling
    While the dewdrops fall,
So I know not who came knocking,
    At all, at all, at all.

THE ELF AND THE DORMOUSE

Oliver Herford

Under a toadstool
   Crept a wee Elf,
Out of the rain
   To shelter himself.

Under the toadstool,
   Sound asleep,
Sat a big Dormouse
   All in a heap.

Trembled the wee Elf,
   Frightened, and yet
Fearing to fly away
   Lest he get wet.

To the next shelter —
   Maybe a mile!
Sudden the wee Elf
   Smiled a wee smile,

Tugged till the toadstool
   Toppled in two.
Holding it over him
   Gaily he flew.

Soon he was safe home
　　Dry as could be.
Soon woke the Dormouse —
　　"Good gracious me!

Where is my toadstool?"
　　Loud he lamented.
— And that's how umbrellas,
　　First were invented.

THE GNOME

Harry Behn

I saw a gnome
As plain as plain
Sitting on top
Of a weathervane.

He was dressed like a crow
In silky black feathers,
And there he sat watching
All kinds of weathers.

He talked like a crow too,
Caw caw caw,
When he told me exactly
What he saw,

Snow to the north of him
Sun to the south,
And he spoke with a beaky
Kind of a mouth.

But he wasn't a crow,
That was plain as plain
'Cause crows never sit
On a weathervane.

What I saw was simply
A usual gnome
Looking things over
On his way home.

THE LITTLE ELFMAN

John K. Bangs

I met a little Elf-man, once,
Down where the lilies blow.
I asked him why he was so small,
And why he didn't grow.

He slightly frowned, and with his eye
He looked me through and through.
"I'm quite as big for me," said he,
"As you are big for you."

287

AN EXPLANATION OF THE GRASSHOPPER

Vachel Lindsay

The Grasshopper, the Grasshopper,
I will explain to you: —
He is the Brownies' racehorse,
The Fairies' Kangaroo.

THE TREE STANDS VERY STRAIGHT AND STILL

Annette Wynne

The tree stands very straight and still
All night long far on the hill;
But if I go and listen near
A million little sounds I hear,
The leaves are little whispering elves
Talking, playing by themselves,
Playing softly altogether
In the warm or windy weather,
Talking softly to the sky
Or any bird that dartles by,
O little elves within the tree,
Is there no word to tell to me?

ONE DAY WHEN WE WENT WALKING

Valine Hobbs

One day when we went walking,
  I found a dragon's tooth,
  A dreadful dragon's tooth.
  "A locust thorn," said Ruth.

One day when we went walking
  I found a brownie's shoe,
  A brownie's button shoe.
  "A dry pea pod," said Sue.

One day when we went walking,
  I found a mermaid's fan,
  A merry mermaid's fan.
  "A scallop shell," said Dan.

One day when we went walking,
  I found a fairy's dress,
  A fairy's flannel dress.
  "A mullein leaf," said Bess.

Next time that I go walking —
  Unles I meet an elf,
  A funny friendly elf —
  I'm going by myself!

289

COULD IT HAVE BEEN A SHADOW?

Monica Shannon

What ran under the rosebush?
What ran under the stone?
Could it have been a shadow,
Running away alone?
Maybe a fairy's shadow,
Slipping away at dawn
To guard a gleaming pot of gold
For a busy leprechaun.

FAIRIES

Rose Fyleman

There are fairies at the bottom of our garden!
It's not so very, very far away;
You pass the gardener's shed and you just keep straight
ahead —
I do so hope they've really come to stay.
There's a little wood, with moss in it and beetles,
And a little stream that quietly runs through;
You wouldn't think they'd dare to come merry-making
there —
Well, they do.

There are fairies at the bottom of our garden!
   They often have a dance on summer nights;
The butterflies and bees make a lovely little breeze,
   And the rabbits stand about and hold the lights.
Did you know that they could sit upon the moonbeams
   And pick a little star to make a fan,
And dance away up there in the middle of the air?
   Well, they can.

There are fairies at the bottom of our garden!
   You cannot think how beautiful they are;
They all stand up and sing when the Fairy Queen and King
   Come gently floating down upon their car.
The King is very proud and *very* handsome;
   The Queen — now can you guess who that could be
(She's a little girl all day, but at night she steals away)
   Well — it's Me!

HAVE YOU WATCHED THE FAIRIES?

Rose Fyleman

Have you watched the fairies when the rain is done
Spreading out their little wings to dry them in the sun?
   I have, I have! Isn't it fun?

Have you heard the fairies all among the limes
Singing little fairy tunes to little fairy rhymes?
I have, I have, lots and lots of times!

Have you seen the fairies dancing in the air,
And dashing off behind the stars to tidy up their hair?
I have, I have; I've been there!

I KEEP THREE WISHES READY

Annette Wynne

I keep three wishes ready,
Lest I should chance to meet,
Any day a fairy
Coming down the street.

I'd hate to have to stammer,
Or have to think them out,
For it's very hard to think things up
When a fairy is about.

And I'd hate to lose my wishes,
For fairies fly away,
And perhaps I'd never have a chance
On any other day.

So I keep three wishes ready,
Lest I should chance to meet,
Any day a fairy
Coming down the street.

A FAIRY WENT A-MARKETING

Rose Fyleman

A fairy went a-marketing —
    She bought a little fish;
She put it in a crystal bowl
    Upon a golden dish.
An hour she sat in wonderment
    And watched its silver gleam,
And then she gently took it up
    And slipped it in a stream.

A fairy went a-marketing —
    She bought a coloured bird;
It sang the sweetest, shrillest song
    That ever she had heard.
She sat beside its painted cage
    And listened half the day,
And then she opened wide the door
    And let it fly away.

A fairy went a-marketing —
  She bought a winter gown
All stitched about with gossamer
  And lined with thistledown.
She wore it all the afternoon
  With prancing and delight,
Then gave it to a little frog
  To keep him warm at night.

A fairy went a-marketing —
  She bought a gentle mouse
To take her tiny messages,
  To keep her tiny house.
All day she kept its busy feet
  Pit-patting to and fro,
And then she kissed its silken ears,
Thanked it, and let it go.

THE BEST GAME THE FAIRIES PLAY

Rose Fyleman

The best game the fairies play,
  The best game of all,
Is sliding down steeples —
  (You know they're very tall.)
You fly to the weathercock,
  And when you hear it crow
You fold your wings and clutch your things
  And then let go!

They have a million other games —
    Cloud-catching's one,
And mud-mixing after rain
    Is heaps and heaps of fun;
But when you go and stay with them
    Never mind the rest,
Take may advice — they're very nice,
    But steeple-sliding's best!

STOCKING FAIRY

Winifred Welles

In a hole of the heel of an old brown stocking,
A little old Fairy sits rocking and rocking,
And scolding and pointing and squeaking and squinting,
Brown as a nut, a bright eye glinting,
She tugs at a thread, she drags up a needle,
She stamps and she shrills, she commences to wheedle,
To whine of the cold, in a fine gust of temper
She beats on my thumb, and then with a whimper
She sulks in her shawl, she says I've forgotten
I promised to make her a lattice of cotton,
A soft, woven window, cozy yet airy,
Where she could sit rocking and peeking — Hush, Fairy,
Tush, Fairy, sit gently, look sweetly,
I'll do what I said, now, and close you in neatly.

SKIPPING ALONG ALONE

Winifred Welles

Oh, how I love to skip alone
   Along the beach in moisty weather;
The whole world seems my very own,
Each fluted shell and glistening stone,
   Each wave that twirls a silver feather.

I skip along so brave and big
   Behind the sand-birds gray and tiny,
I love to see their quick feet jig,
Each leaves a mark, neat as a twig,
   Stamped in the sand so clear and shiny.

And fine and faint as drops of spray
   I hear their little voices calling,
"Sweet, sweet! Sweet, sweet!" I hear them say —
I love to skip alone and play
   Along the sand when mist is falling.

WHITE HORSES

Winifred Howard

Little white horses are out on the sea,
   Bridled with rainbows and speckled with foam,

Laden with presents for you and for me;
   Mermaids and fairies are riding them home!
            Gold from the sun;
            Diamonds rare
            Made from dew
            And frosty air;
            Veils of mist,
            Soft and white,
            Rose and silver,
            Shimmering, bright;
            Sweetest perfumes,
            Colored shells,
            Lilting music,
            Fairy bells:
Fairies and mermaids are bringing them home
On Little White Horses all speckled with foam.

THE SEA PRINCESS

Katharine Pyle

         In a garden of shining sea-weed,
            Set round with twisted shells,
         Under the deeps of the ocean,
            The little sea princess dwells.

         Sometimes she sees the shadow
            Of a great whale passing by,
         Or a white-winged vessel sailing
            Between the sea and sky.

297

Without the palace, her sea-horse
  Feeds in his crystal stall,
And fishes, with scales that glisten,
  Come leaping forth at her call.

And when the day has faded
  From over the lonesome deep,
In a shell as smooth as satin
  The princess is rocked to sleep.

IN THE MOONLIGHT

Norreys Jepson O'Conor

The Fairies dance the livelong night
Across the moonlit hill;
The moonbeams dance along the lake;
The western wind is still.
The waters make a little sound
More sweet than music far —
Oh, let me fly across the world
To where the Fairies are!

A FAIRY VOYAGE

Unknown

> If I were just a fairy small,
>   I'd take a leaf and sail away,
> I'd sit astride the stem and guide
>   It straight to Fairyland and stay.

I'D LOVE TO BE A FAIRY'S CHILD

Robert Graves

> Children born of fairy stock
> Never need for shirt or frock,
> Never want for food or fire,
> Always get their heart's desire:
> Jingle pockets full of gold,
> Marry when they're seven years old.
> Every fairy child may keep
> Two strong ponies and ten sheep;
> All have houses, each his own,
> Built of brick or granite stone;
> They live on cherries, they run wild —
> I'd love to be a Fairy's child.

VERY NEARLY

Queenie Scott-Hopper

I never quite saw fairy-folk
   A-dancing in the glade,
Where, just beyond the hollow oak,
   Their broad green rings are laid;
But, while behind that oak I hid,
One day I very nearly did!

I never quite saw mermaids rise
   Above the twilight sea,
When sands, left wet, 'neath sunset skies,
   Are blushing rosily:
But — all alone, those rocks amid —
One day I very nearly did!

I never quite saw Goblin Grim,
   Who haunts our lumber room
And pops his head above the rim
   Of that oak chest's deep gloom:
But once — when Mother raised the lid —
I very, very nearly did!

WAS SHE A WITCH?

Laura E. Richards

There was an old woman
    Lived down in a dell;
She used to draw picklejacks
    Out of the well.
How did she do it?
Nobody knew it,
    She never, no never, no never would tell.

GODMOTHER

Phyllis B. Morden

There was an old lady
Who had three faces,
One for everyday,
And one for wearing places —
To meetings and parties,
Dull places like that —
A face that looked well
With a grown-up hat.
But she carried in her pocket
The face of an elf,

And she'd clap it on quick
When she felt like herself.
Sitting in the parlor
Of somebody's house,
She'd reach in her pocket
Sly as a mouse . . .
And there in the corner,
Sipping her tea,
Was a laughing elf-woman
Nobody could see!

THE SUGAR-PLUM TREE

Eugene Field

Have you ever heard of the Sugar-Plum Tree?
'Tis a marvel of great renown!
It blooms on the shore of the Lollipop Sea
In the garden of Shut-Eye Town;
The fruit that it bears is so wondrously sweet
(As those who have tasted it say)
That the good little children have only to eat
Of that fruit to be happy next day.

When you've got to the tree, you would have a hard time
To capture the fruit which I sing;
The tree is so tall that no person could climb
To the boughs where the sugar-plums swing!
But up in that tree sits a chocolate cat,
And a gingerbread dog prowls below —
And this is the way you contrive to get at
Those sugar-plums tempting you so:

You say but the word to that gingerbread dog
And he barks with such terrible zest
And the chocolate cat is at once all agog,
As her swelling portions attest.
And the chocolate cat goes cavorting around
From this leafy limb unto that,
And the sugar-plums tumble, of course, to the ground —
Hurrah for that chocolate cat!

There are marshmallows, gumdrops, and peppermint canes,
With striplings of scarlet or gold,
And you carry away of the treasure that rains
As much as your apron can hold!

Changing

Seasons

THE SEASONS

Mother Goose

Spring is showery, flowery, bowery;
Summer: hoppy, croppy, poppy,
Autumn: wheezy, sneezy, freezy;
Winter: slippy, drippy, nippy.

DIRECTIONS

Onitsura

Eyes, side-to-side;
nose, up-and-down.
Spring flowers!

DAFFODILS

Unknown

In spite of cold and chills
That usher in the early spring,
We have the daffodils.

DAFFADOWNDILLY

Mother Goose

Daffadowndilly
　Has come up to town,
In a yellow petticoat
　And a green gown.

HOW THE FLOWERS GROW

Gabriel Setoun

This is how the flowers grow:
I have watched them and I know.

First, above the ground is seen
A tiny blade of purest green,
Reaching up and peeping forth
East and west and south and north.

Then it shoots up day by day,
Circling in a curious way
Round a blossom, which it keeps
Warm and cozy while it sleeps.

Then the sunbeams find their way
To the sleeping bud and say,
"We are children of the sun
Sent to wake thee, little one."

And the leaflet opening wide
Shows the tiny bud inside,
Peeping with half-opened eye
On the bright and sunny sky.

Breezes from the west and south
Lay their kisses on its mouth;
Till the petals all are grown,
And the bud's a flower blown.

This is how the flowers grow:
I have watched them and I know.

LITTLE GRAY PUSSY

Unknown

I have a little pussy,
    And her coat is silver gray;
She lives in a great wide meadow,
    And she never runs away.

She always is a pussy,
    She'll never be a cat
Because — she's a pussy willow!
    Now what do you think of that!

CITY RAIN

Rachel Field

Rain in the city!
    I love to see it fall
Slant wise where the buildings crowd
    Red brick and all.
Streets of shiny wetness
    Where the taxis go,
With people and umbrellas all
    Bobbing to and fro.

Rain in the city!
    I love to hear it drip
When I am cosy in my room
    Snug as any ship,
With toys spread on the table,
    With picture book or two,
And the rain like a rumbling tune that sings
    Through everything I do.

IN TIME OF SILVER RAIN

Langston Hughes

In time of silver rain
The earth
Puts forth new life again,
Green grasses grow
And flowers lift their heads,
And over all the plain
The wonder spreads
      Of life,
      Of life,
      Of life!

In time of silver rain
The butterflies
Lift silken wings
To catch a rainbow cry,
And trees put forth
New leaves to sing
In joy beneath the sky
As down the roadway
Passing boys and girls
Go singing, too,
In time of silver rain
      When spring
      And life
      Are new.

IT IS RAINING

Lucy Sprague Mitchell

It is raining.

Where would you like to be in the rain?
Where would you like to be?

I'd like to be on a city street,
where the rain comes down in a driving sheet,
where it wets the houses — roof and wall —
the wagons and horses and autos and all.
That's where I'd like to be in the rain,
that's where I'd like to be.

It is raining.

Where would you like to be in the rain?
Where would you like to be?

I'd like to be in a tall tree top,
where the rain comes dripping, drop, drop, drop,
around on every side:
where it wets the farmer, the barn, the pig,
the cows, the chickens both little and big;
where it batters and beats on a field of wheat
and makes the little birds hide.

It is raining.

Where would you like to be in the rain?
Where would you like to be?

I'd like to be on a ship at sea,
where everything's wet as wet can be
and the waves are rolling high,
where sailors are pulling the ropes and singing,
and wind's in the rigging and salt spray's stinging,
and round us sea gulls cry.
On a dipping, skimming ship at sea —
that's where I'd like to be in the rain;
that's where I'd like to be!

RAIN

Robert Louis Stevenson

The rain is raining all around,
It falls on field and tree,
It rains on the umbrellas here,
And on the ships at sea.

WHO IS TAPPING AT MY WINDOW

A. G. Deming

"It's not I," said the cat.
"It's not I," said the rat.

"It's not I," said the wren.
"It's not I," said the hen.

"It's not I," said the fox.
"It's not I," said the ox.

"It's not I," said the loon.
"It's not I," said the coon.

"It's not I," said the cony.
"It's not I," said the pony.

"It's not I," said the dog.
"It's not I," said the frog.

"It's not I," said the hare.
"It's not I," said the bear.

"It is I," said the rain.
"Tapping at your windowpane."

DOWN THE RAIN FALLS

Elizabeth Coatsworth

> Down the rain falls,
> Up crackles the fire,
> Tick-tock goes the clock
> Neither lower nor higher —
>
> Such soft little sounds
> As sleepy hens make
> When they talk to themselves
> For company's sake.

RAIN RIDERS

Clinton Scollard

> Last night I heard a *rat-tat-too;*
>   'Twas not a drum-beat, that was plain;
> I listened long, and then I knew
>   It was the Riders of the Rain.
>
> But with the rising of the dawn
>   There was no sound of any hoofs;
> The Riders of the Rain had gone
>   To tramp on other children's roofs.

314

VERY LOVELY

Rose Fyleman

Wouldn't it be lovely if the rain came down
Till the water was quite high over all the town?
If the cabs and buses all were set afloat,
And we had to go to school in a little boat?

Wouldn't it be lovely if it still should pour
And we all went up to live on the second floor?
If we saw the butcher sailing up the hill,
And we took the letters in at the window sill?

It's been raining, raining, all the afternoon;
All these things might happen really very soon.
If we woke tomorrow and found they had begun,
Wouldn't it be glorious? *Wouldn't* it be fun?

RAIN, RAIN, GO AWAY

Unknown

Rain, rain, go away,
Come again another day;
Little Johnny wants to play.

THE RAINBOW

David McCord

The rainbow arches in the sky,
But in the earth it ends;
And if you ask the reason why,
They'll tell you "That depends."

It never comes without the rain,
Nor goes without the sun;
And though you try with might and main,
You'll never catch me one.

Perhaps you'll see it once a year,
Perhaps you'll say: "No, twice";
But every time it does appear,
It's very clean and nice.

If I were God, I'd like to win
At sun-and-moon croquet:
I'd drive the rainbow-wickets in
And ask someone to play.

THE WINTER IS PAST

The Bible

> For, lo, the winter is past,
> The rain is over and gone;
> The flowers appear on the earth;
> The time of the singing of birds is come,
> And the voice of the turtle is heard in our land.

MARCH WINDS

Mother Goose

> March winds and April showers
> Bring forth May flowers.

THE MERRY MONTH OF MARCH

William Wordsworth

> The cock is crowing,
> The stream is flowing,
> The small birds twitter,
> The lake doth glitter,
> The green field sleeps in the sun;
> The oldest and youngest

Are at work with the strongest;
The cattle are grazing,
Their heads never raising;
There are forty feeding like one!

Like an army defeated
The snow hath retreated,
And now doth fare ill
On the top of the bare hill;
The Plough-boy is whooping anon, anon.
There's joy in the mountains;
There's life in the fountains;
Small clouds are sailing,
Blue sky prevailing;
The rain is over and gone!

THE COMING OF SPRING

Nora Perry

There's something in the air
That's new and sweet and rare —
A scent of summer things,
A whirr as if of wings.

There's something too that's new
In the color of the blue
That's in the morning sky,
Before the sun is high.

And though on plain and hill,
'Tis winter, winter still,
There's something seems to say
That winter's had its day.

APRIL

Sara Teasdale

The roofs are shining from the rain,
  The sparrows twitter as they fly,
And with a windy April grace
  The little clouds go by.

Yet the back-yards are bare and brown
  With only one unchanging tree —
I could not be so sure of Spring
  Save that it sings in me.

A SUMMER MORNING

Rachel Field

I saw dawn creep across the sky,
And all the gulls go flying by.
I saw the sea put on its dress
Of blue mid-summer loveliness,
And heard the trees begin to stir

319

Green arms of pine and juniper.
I heard the wind call out and say:
"Get up, my dear, it is to-day."

UP THE BARLEY ROWS

Sōra

Up the barley rows,
    Stitching, Stitching them together,
        a butterfly goes.

PLAY ABOUT, DO

Baskō

Play about, do,
    from grass-leaf to grass-leaf!
        Jewels of dew!

I'M GLAD THE SKY IS PAINTED BLUE

Unknown

I'm glad the sky is painted blue,
    And the earth is painted green,
With such a lot of nice fresh air
    All sandwiched in between.

LITTLE RAIN

Elizabeth Madox Roberts

When I was making myself a game
Up in the garden, a little rain came.

It fell down quick in a sort of rush,
And I crawled under the snowball bush.

I could hear the big drops hit the ground
And see little puddles of dust fly round.

A chicken came till the rain was gone;
He had just a very few feathers on.

He shivered a little under his skin,
And then he shut his eyeballs in.

Even after the rain had begun to hush
It kept on raining up in the bush.

One big flat drop came sliding down,
And a ladybug that was red and brown

Was up on a little stem waiting there,
And I got some rain in my hair.

COLOR

Christina Rossetti

What is pink? a rose is pink
By a fountain's brink.
What is red? a poppy's red
In its barley bed.
What is blue? the sky is blue
Where the clouds float thro'.
What is white? a swan is white
Sailing in the light.
What is yellow? pears are yellow
Rich and ripe and mellow.
What is green? the grass is green,
With small flowers between.
What is violet? clouds are violet
In the summer twilight.
What is orange? Why, an orange,
Just an orange!

CLOUDS

Dorothy Aldis

If I had a spoon
As tall as the sky
I'd dish out the clouds
That go slip-sliding by.

I'd take them right in
And give them to cook
And see if they tasted
As good as they look.

THIRTY DAYS HATH SEPTEMBER

Unknown

Thirty days hath September,
April, June, and November;
February has twenty-eight alone,
All the rest have thirty-one,
Excepting leap year; that's the time
When February's days are twenty-nine.

MAPLE LEAVES

Shiko

Envied by us all,
     turning to such loveliness —
          red leaves that fall.

AN INDIAN SUMMER DAY ON THE PRAIRIE

Vachel Lindsay

IN THE BEGINNING
The sun is a huntress young,
The sun is a red, red joy,
The sun is an Indian girl,
Of the tribe of the Illinois.

MID-MORNING
The sun is a smoldering fire,
That creeps through the high gray plain,
And leaves not a bush of cloud
To blossom with flowers of rain.

NOON
The sun is a wounded deer,
That treads pale grass in the skies,
Shaking his golden horns,
Flashing his baleful eyes.

SUNSET
The sun is an eagle old,
There in the windless west,
Atop of the spirit-cliffs
He builds him a crimson nest.

DOWN! DOWN!

Eleanor Farjeon

> Down, Down!
> Yellow and brown
> The leaves are falling over the town.

THE LEAVES DO NOT MIND AT ALL

Annette Wynne

> The leaves do not mind at all
> That they must fall.
> When summertime has gone,
> It is pleasant to put on
> A traveling coat of brown and gray
> And fly away,
> Past the barn and past the school,
> Past the noisy little pool
> It used to hear but could not see.
> Oh, it is joy to be
> A leaf — and free!
> To be swiftly on the wing
> Like a bird adventuring.
> And then, tired out, to creep
> Under some friendly rail and go to sleep;
> The leaves do not mind at all
> That they must fall.

THE MONKEY'S RAINCOAT

Bashō

> The first cold showers pour.
> Even the monkey seems to want
> a little coat of straw.

BROOMS

Dorothy Aldis

> On stormy days
> When the wind is high
> Tall trees are brooms
> Sweeping the sky.
>
> They swish their branches
> In buckets of rain,
> And swash and sweep it
> Blue again.

THE MOON'S THE NORTH WIND'S COOKY

Vachel Lindsay

The Moon's the North Wind's cooky.
He bites it, day by day,
Until there's but a rim of scraps
That crumble all away.

The South Wind is a baker.
He kneads clouds in his den,
And bakes a crisp new moon *that . . . greedy*
North . . . Wind . . . eats . . . again!

WIND IS A CAT

Ethel Romig Fuller

Wind is a cat
    That prowls at night,
Now in a valley,
    Now on a height,

Pouncing on houses
    Till folks in their beds
Draw all the covers
    Over their heads.

It sings to the moon
 It scratches at doors;
It lashes its tail
 Around chimneys and roars.

It claws at the clouds
 Till it fringes their silk,
It laps up the dawn
 Like a saucer of milk;

Then, chasing the stars
 To the tops of the firs,
Curls down for a nap
 And purrs and purrs.

FOG

Carl Sandburg

The fog comes
on little cat feet.

It sits looking
over harbor and city
on silent haunches
and then moves on.

THE MIST AND ALL

Dixie Willson

I like the fall,
The mist and all.
I like the night owl's
Lonely call —
And wailing sound
Of wind around.

I like the gray
November day,
And bare, dead boughs
That coldly sway
Against my pane.
I like the rain.

I like to sit
And laugh at it —
And tend
My cozy fire a bit.
I like the fall —
The mist and all.

JACK FROST

Helen Bayley Davis

Someone painted pictures on my
Window pane last night —
Willow trees with trailing boughs
And flowers — frosty white
And lovely crystal butterflies;
But when the morning sun
Touched them with its golden beams,
They vanished one by one!

LITTLE JACK FROST

Unknown

Little Jack Frost went up the hill,
Watching the stars and moon so still,
Watching the stars and moon so bright,
And laughing aloud with all his might.

Little Jack Frost ran down the hill,
Late in the night when the winds were still,
Late in the fall when the leaves fell down,
Red and yellow and faded brown.

Little Jack Frost walked through the trees,
"Oh," sighed the flowers, "we freeze, we freeze,"
"Oh," cried the grasses, "we die, we die."
Said Little Jack Frost, "Good-by, good-by."

Little Jack Frost went round and round,
Spreading white snow on the frozen ground,
Nipping the breezes, icing the streams,
And chilling the warmth of the sun's bright beams.

But when Dame Nature brought back the spring,
Brought back the birds to chirp and sing,
Melted the snow and warmed the sky,
Then Little Jack Frost went pouting by.

The flowers opened their eyes of blue,
Green buds peeped out and grasses grew.
It was so warm and scorched him so,
That Little Jack Frost was glad to go.

SOMETHING TOLD THE WILD GEESE

Rachel Field

Something told the wild geese
    It was time to go.
Though the fields lay golden
    Something whispered, — "Snow."

Leaves were green and stirring,
   Berries, luster-glossed,
But beneath warm feathers
   Something cautioned, — "Frost."
All the sagging orchards
   Steamed with amber spice,
But each wild breast stiffened
   At remembered ice.
Something told the wild geese
   It was time to fly, —
Summer sun was on their wings,
   Winter in their cry.

FOOTWEAR

May Justus

The rain has silver sandals
   For dancing in the spring
And shoes with golden tassels
   For summer's frolicking.
Her winter boots have hobnails
   Of ice from heel to toe,
Which now and then she changes
   For moccasins of snow.

FIRST SNOW

Marie Louise Allen

Snow makes whiteness where it falls.
The bushes look like popcorn-balls.
The places where I always play,
Look like somewhere else today.

NO SKY AT ALL

Hashin

No sky at all;
    no earth at all — and still
        the snowflakes fall. . . .

WINTER

Jean Jaszi

See the far hills white with snow
See the river black below
See the bare trees
See the land —
Wearing mittens
Like my hand.

FIRST WINTER'S DAY

Dorothy Aldis

Frosted over with cold flakes,
Cars and buses look like cakes.

A milk horse scrunches up the street,
His eyelashes are white with sleet.

Around the corner here we blow,
Our faces tickled by the snow.

The snow makes snow caps for our heads.
Tomorrow we will slide our sleds.

OUTSIDE THE DOOR

Annette Wynne

Outside the door the bare tree stands,
And catches snowflakes in its hands,
And holds them well and holds them high,
Until a puffing wind comes by.

WHITE FIELDS

James Stephens

In the wintertime we go
Walking in the fields of snow;

Where there is no grass at all;
Where the top of every wall,

Every fence and every tree,
Is as white as white can be.

Pointing out the way we came,
Every one of them the same —

All across the fields there be
Prints in silver filigree;

And our mothers always know,
By the footprints in the snow,

Where it is the children go.

FALLING SNOW

Unknown

See the pretty snowflakes.
Falling from the sky;
On the walk and housetop
Soft and thick they lie.

On the window-ledges
On the branches bare
Now how fast they gather,
Filling all the air.

Looking in the garden,
Where the grass was green;
Covered by the snowflakes,
Not a blade is seen.

Now the bare black bushes
All look soft and white,
Every twig is laden —
What a pretty sight!

THE SNOWMAN'S RESOLUTION

Aileen Fisher

The snowman's hat was crooked
  And his nose was out of place
And several of his whiskers
  Had fallen from his face.

But the snowman didn't notice
  For he was trying to think
Of a New Year's resolution
  That wouldn't melt or shrink.

He thought and planned and pondered
  With his little snow-ball head
Till his eyes began to glisten
  And his toes began to spread;

And at last he said, "I've got it —
  I'll make a firm resolve
That no matter what the weather
  My smile will not dissolve."

Now the snowman acted wisely
  And his resolution won
For his splinter smile was WOODEN
  And it didn't mind the sun!

Wonder
And
Beauty

THE STAR

Jane Taylor

> Twinkle, twinkle, little star,
> How I wonder what you are!
> Up above the world so high
> Like a diamond in the sky.

NIGHT

Sara Teasdale

> Stars over snow,
>   And in the west a planet
> Swinging below a star —
>   Look for a lovely thing and you will find it,
> It is not far —
>   It will never be far.

BEAUTY

Bashō

> The usually hateful crow:
>   he, too — this morning,
>   on the snow!

THE FALLING STAR

Sara Teasdale

I saw a star slide down the sky,
Blinding the north as it went by,
Too lovely to be bought or sold,
Too burning and too quick to hold,
Good only to make wishes on
And then forever to be gone.

THE HORSEMAN

Walter de la Mare

I heard a horseman
   Ride over the hill;
The moon shone clear,
   The night was still;
His helm was silver,
   And pale was he;
And the horse he rode
   Was of ivory.

THE MOON

Ryuho

I scooped up the moon
In my water
Bucket . . . and
Spilled it on the grass

THE MOON IN THE WATER

Ryōta

The moon in the water
turned a somersault
and floated away.

THE BUTTERFLY

Kikaku

A sleeping butterfly!
During the nights,
what can it be he does?

THE NIGHT WILL NEVER STAY

Eleanor Farjeon

The night will never stay,
The night will still go by,
Though with a million stars
You pin it to the sky;
Though you bind it with the blowing wind
And buckle it with the moon,
The night will slip away
Like sorrow or a tune.

MORNING

Emily Dickinson

Will there really be a morning?
Is there such a thing as day?
Could I see it from the mountains
If I were as tall as they?

Has it feet like water-lilies?
Has it feathers like a bird?
Is it brought from famous countries
Of which I have never heard?

343

Oh, some scholar! Oh, some sailor!
Oh, some wise man from the skies!
Please to tell a little pilgrim
Where the place called morning lies!

THE SUN

John Drinkwater

I told the Sun that I was glad,
 I'm sure I don't know why;
Somehow the pleasant way he had
 Of shining in the sky,
Just put a notion in my head
 That wouldn't it be fun
If, walking on the hill, I said
 "I'm happy" to the Sun.

HOW GRAY THE RAIN

Elizabeth Coatsworth

How gray the rain
And gray the world
And gray the rain clouds overhead,
When suddenly
Some cloud is furled
And there is gleaming sun instead!

The raindrops drip
Prismatic light,
And trees and meadows burn in green,
And arched in air
Serene and bright
The rainbow all at once is seen.

Serene and bright
The rainbow stands
That was not anywhere before,
And so may joy
Fill empty hands
When someone enters through a door.

THE RAINBOW

Walter de la Mare

I saw the lovely arch
Of Rainbow span the sky,
The gold sun burning
As the rain swept by.

In bright-ringed solitude
The showery foliage shone
One lovely moment,
And the Bow was gone.

THE RAINBOW

Christina Rossetti

Boats sail on the rivers,
  And ships sail on the seas;
But clouds that sail across the sky
  Are prettier far than these.

There are bridges on the rivers,
  As pretty as you please;
But the bow that bridges heaven,
  And overtops the trees,
And builds a road from earth to sky,
  Is prettier far than these.

MY HEART LEAPS UP

William Wordsworth

My heart leaps up when I behold
  A rainbow in the sky:
So was it when my life began;
So is it now I am a man;
So be it when I shall grow old,
  Or let me die!

PLUM BLOSSOMS

Unknown

So sweet the plum trees smell!
Would that the brush that paints the flower
Could paint the scent as well.

APRIL

Eunice Tietjens

The tulips now are pushing up
Like small green knuckles through the ground.
The grass is young and doubtful yet.
The robin takes a look around.
And if you listen you can hear
Spring laughing with a windy sound.

THE CROCUS

Walter Crane

The golden crocus reaches up
To catch a sunbeam in her cup.

CASUAL GOLD

Maud E. Uschold

> What is lovelier than the gold
> of dandelion, velvet-soft and fringed
> with slender petals,
> flung upon the grass;
> A casual cloth of gold
> where lightly pass
> the delicate feet of Spring.

CALLED AWAY

Richard Le Gallienne

> I meant to do my work today —
> But a brown bird sang in the apple tree,
> And a butterfly flitted across the field,
> And all the leaves were calling me.
>
> And the wind went sighing over the land
> Tossing the grasses to and fro,
> And a rainbow held out its shining hand —
> So what could I do but laugh and go?

348

TREASURES

Mary Dixon Thayer

Down on the beach when the tide is out
Beautiful things lie all about —
Rubies and diamonds and shells and pearls,
Starfish, oysters, and mermaids' curls;
Slabs of black marble cut in the sand,
Veined and smoothed and polished by hand;
And whipped-up foam that I think must be
What mermen use for cream in tea.

These and a million treasures I know
Strew the beach when the tide is low —
But very few people seem to care
For such gems scattered everywhere.
Lots of these jewels I hide away
In an old box I found one day.
And if a beggar asks me for bread
I will give him diamonds instead.

CURIOSITY

Harry Behn

Tell me, tell me everything!
What makes it Winter

349

And then Spring?
Which are the children
Butterflies?
Why do people keep
Winking their eyes?
Where do birds sleep?
Do bees like to sting?
Tell me, tell me please, everything!

Tell me, tell me, I want to know!
What makes leaves grow
In the shapes they grow?
Why do goldfish
Keep chewing? and rabbits
Warble their noses?
Just from habits?
Where does the wind
When it goes away go?
Tell me! or don't even grown-ups know?

AFTERNOON ON A HILL

Edna St. Vincent Millay

I will be the gladdest thing
Under the sun!
I will touch a hundred flowers
And not pick one.

I will look at cliffs and clouds
　　With quiet eyes,
Watch the wind bow down the grass,
　　And the grass rise.

And when lights begin to show
　　Up from the town,
I will mark which must be mine,
　　And then start down!

WATCHING CLOUDS

John Farrar

I've watched the clouds by day and night,
Great fleecy ones all filled with light,
Gray beasts that steal across the sky,
And little fellows slipping by.

Sometimes they seem like sheep at play,
Sometimes when they are dull and gray
The pale sun seems a ship to me,
Sailing through a rolling sea;

And I've seen faces in them, too,
Funny white men on the blue;
But on across the heavens they blow —
I often wonder where they go.

CLOUDS

Unknown

White sheep, white sheep,
   On a blue hill,
When the wind stops,
   You all stand still.

When the wind blows,
   You walk away slow.
White sheep, white sheep,
   Where do you go?

I HEARD A BIRD SING

Oliver Herford

I heard a bird sing
   In the dark of December
A magical thing
   And sweet to remember.

"We are nearer to Spring
   Than we were in September,"
I heard a bird sing
   In the dark of December.

THE WIND

Robert Louis Stevenson

I saw you toss the kites on high
And blow the birds about the sky;
And all around I heard you pass,
Like ladies' skirts across the grass —
   O wind, a-blowing all day long,
   O wind, that sings so loud a song!

I saw the different things you did,
But always you yourself you hid.
I felt you push, I heard you call,
I could not see yourself at all —
   O wind, a-blowing all day long,
   O wind, that sings so loud a song!

O you that are so strong and cold,
O blower, are you young or old?
Are you a beast of field and tree,
Or just a stronger child than me?
   O wind, a-blowing all day long,
   O wind, that sings so loud a song!

VELVET SHOES

Elinor Wylie

Let us walk in the white snow
   In a soundless space;
With footsteps quiet and slow,
   At a tranquil pace,
   Under veils of white lace.

I shall go shod in silk,
   And you in wool,
White as a white cow's milk,
   More beautiful
   Than the breast of a gull.

We shall walk through the still town
   In a windless peace;
We shall step upon white down,
   Upon silver fleece,
   Upon softer than these.

We shall walk in velvet shoes:
   Wherever we go
Silence will fall like dews
   On white silence below.
   We shall walk in the snow.

OTHERWISE

Aileen Fisher

There must be magic,
Otherwise,
How could day turn to night,

And how could sailboats,
Otherwise,
Go sailing out of sight,

And how could peanuts,
Otherwise,
Be covered up so tight?

FEBRUARY TWILIGHT

Sara Teasdale

I stood beside a hill
  Smooth with new-laid snow,
A single star looked out
  From the cold evening glow.

There was no other creature
  That saw what I could see —
I stood and watched the evening star
  As long as it watched me.

HOLD FAST YOUR DREAMS

Louise Driscoll

Hold fast your dreams!
Within your heart
Keep one still, secret spot
Where dreams may go,
And sheltered so,
May thrive and grow —
Where doubt and fear are not.
Oh, keep a place apart
Within your heart,
For little dreams to go.

A PRAYER

Unknown

Father, we thank Thee for the night
And for the pleasant morning light,
For rest and food and loving care,
And all that makes the world so fair.
Help us to do the things we should,
To be to others kind and good,
In all we do, in all we say,
To grow more loving every day.

THE UNICORN

Ella Young

While yet the Morning Star
Flamed in the sky
A Unicorn went mincing by,
Whiter by far than blossom of the thorn:
His silver horn
Glittered as he danced and pranced
Silver-pale in the silver-pale morn.

The folk that saw him, ran away.

Where he went, so gay, so fleet,
Star-like lilies at his feet
Flowered all day,
Lilies, lilies in a throng,
And the wind made for him a song:

But he dared not stay
Over-long!

Shining

Days

NEW YEAR'S DAY

Rachel Field

Last night while we were fast asleep,
The old year went away.
It can't come back again because
A new one's come to stay.

A SURE SIGN

Nancy Byrd Turner

Here's the mail, sort it quick —
Papers, letters, notes,
Postcard scenes,
Magazines;
Our hearts are in our throats.
Something there,
White and square,
Sealed with wax, and bumpy —
At the edges flat and thin,
In the middle lumpy.
When you feel the envelope,
Do your fingers trace
Something narrow,
Like an arrow?
Or a part
Of a heart?

Or a Cupid's face?
Is your name across the back
In a crooked line?
Hurry, then; that's a sign
Someone's sent a valentine!

TO MY VALENTINE

Unknown

If apples were pears,
And peaches were plums,
And the rose had a different name, —
If tigers were bears,
And fingers were thumbs,
I'd love you just the same!

MY VALENTINE

Kitty Parsons

I have a little valentine
That someone sent to me.
It's pink and white and red and blue,
And pretty as can be.

Forget-me-nots are round the edge,
And tiny roses, too;

And such a lovely piece of lace —
The very palest blue.

And in the center there's a heart
As red as red can be!
And on it's written all in gold,
"To you, with Love from Me."

WASHINGTON

Nancy Byrd Turner

He played by the river when he was young,
He raced with rabbits along the hills,
He fished for minnows, and climbed and swung,
And hooted back at the whippoorwills.
Strong and slender and tall he grew —
And then, one morning, the bugles blew.

Over the hills the summons came,
Over the river's shining rim.
He said that the bugles called his name,
He knew that his country needed him,
And he answered, "Coming!" and marched away
For many a night and many a day.

Perhaps when the marches were hot and long
He'd think of the river flowing by

Or, camping under the winter sky,
Would hear the whippoorwill's far-off song.
At work, at play, and in peace or strife,
He loved America all his life!

DOWN A SUNNY EASTER MEADOW

Nancy Byrd Turner

Down a sunny Easter meadow
Went a rabbit, running sprightly;
With him went his skippy shadow.
Tag they played, and played it lightly.

All the robins in the meadow
Called to them as they jumped and scurried,
"Hurry, Bunny! Hurry, Shadow!

Easter's coming!"

And they hurried.

IF EASTER EGGS WOULD HATCH

Douglas Malloch

I wish that Easter eggs would do
   Like eggs of other seasons:
I wish that they hatched something, too,
   For — well, for lots of reasons.
The eggs you get the usual way
   Are always gay and bright ones.

I'd love to see a purple hen,
   A rooster like a bluebird,
For that would make an old bird then
   Look really like a new bird.
If Easter eggs hatched like the rest,
   The robin and the swallow
Would peek inside a chicken's nest
   To see what styles to follow.

The rooster now is pretty proud,
   But wouldn't he be merry
If roosters only were allowed
   To dress like some canary!
And wouldn't it be fun to catch
   A little silver bunny!
If Easter eggs would only hatch,
My, wouldn't that be funny!

MEETING THE EASTER BUNNY

Rowena Bennett

On Easter morn at early dawn
   before the cocks were crowing,
I met a bob-tail bunnykin
   and asked where he was going,
"'Tis in the house and out the house
   a-tipsy, tipsy-toeing,
'Tis round the house and 'bout the house
   a-lightly I am going."
"But what is that of every hue
   you carry in your basket?"
"'Tis eggs of gold and eggs of blue;
   I wonder that you ask it.
'Tis chocolate eggs and bonbon eggs
   and eggs of red and gray,
For every child in every house
   on bonny Easter Day."
He perked his ears and winked his eye
   and twitched his little nose;
He shook his tail — what tail he had —
   and stood up on his toes.
"I must be gone before the sun;
   the east is growing gray;
'Tis almost time for bells to chime." —
   So he hippety-hopped away.

EASTER

Joyce Kilmer

The air is like a butterfly
    With frail blue wings.
The happy earth looks at the sky
    And sings.

SOME THINGS THAT EASTER BRINGS

Elsie Parrish

Easter duck and Easter chick,
Easter eggs with chocolate thick.

Easter hats for one and all,
Easter Bunny makes a call!

Happy Easter always brings
Such a lot of pleasant things.

ALL FOOLS' DAY

Unknown

The first of April, some do say
Is set apart for All Fools' Day;
But why the people call it so
Nor I, nor they themselves do know
But on this day are people sent
On purpose for pure merriment.

APRIL FOOL

Eleanor Hammond

Small April sobbed,
"I'm going to cry!
Please give me a cloud
To wipe my eye!"

Then, "April fool!"
She laughed instead
And smiled a rainbow
Overhead!

TREES

Harry Behn

Trees are the kindest things I know,
They do no harm, they simply grow

And spread a shade for sleepy cows,
And gather birds among their boughs.

They give us fruit in leaves above,
And wood to make our houses of,

And leaves to burn on Hallowe'en,
And in the Spring new buds of green.

They are the first when day's begun
To touch the beams of morning sun,

They are the last to hold the light
When evening changes into night,

And when a moon floats on the sky
They hum a drowsy lullaby

Of sleepy children long ago . . .
Trees are the kindest things I know.

BLACK AND GOLD

Nancy Byrd Turner

Everything is black and gold,
  Black and gold, tonight:
Yellow pumpkins, yellow moon,
  Yellow candlelight;

Jet-black cat with golden eyes,
  Shadows black as ink,
Firelight blinking in the dark
  With a yellow blink.

Black and gold, black and gold,
  Nothing in between —
When the world turns black and gold,
  Then it's Hallowe'en!

RIDDLE: WHAT AM I?

Dorothy Aldis

They chose me from my brothers:
"That's the nicest one," they said,
And they carved me out a face and put a
Candle in my head;

And they set me on the doorstep.
Oh, the night was dark and wild;
But when they lit the candle, then I
Smiled!

IF YOU'VE NEVER

Elsie M. Fowler

If you've never seen an old witch
Riding through the sky —
Or never felt big bat's wings
Flopping, as they fly —
If you've never touched a white thing
Gliding through the air,
And knew it was a ghost because
You got a dreadful scare —
If you've never heard the night owls,
Crying, "Whoo-whoo-whoo?"
And never jumped at pumpkin eyes
Gleaming out at you —
If all of these exciting things
You've never heard nor seen,
Why then — you've missed a lot of fun,
Because—that's *Hallowe'en!*

JACK O'LANTERN

Anna Chandler Ayre

The man in the moon looked down on the field,
    Where the golden pumpkin lay;
He winked at him, and he blinked at him,
    In the funniest kind of way.

But on Halloween, when the moon looked down
    From the sky, through the shadows dim,
The pumpkin fat on a gatepost sat,
    And saucily laughed at him.

LITANY FOR HALLOWEEN

Unknown

From Ghoulies and Ghosties,
Long-leggety Beasties,
And THINGS
That go BUMP in the night,
Good Lord, deliver us!

371

THANKSGIVING TIME

Unknown

When all the leaves are off the boughs,
   And nuts and apples gathered in,
And cornstalks waiting for the cows,
   And pumpkins safe in barn and bin;

Then Mother says: "My children dear,
   The fields are brown and autumn flies;
Thanksgiving Day is very near,
   And we must make Thanksgiving pies!"

RIDDLE

Christina Rossetti

First it was a pretty flower, dressed in
   pink and white,
Then it was a tiny ball, almost hid
   from sight.
Round and green and large it grew —
   then it turned to red.
It will make a splendid pie for your
   Thanksgiving Spread.

               (An apple)

THANKSGIVING

Ralph Waldo Emerson

For flowers that bloom about our feet,
    Father, we thank Thee,
For tender grass so fresh and sweet,
    Father, we thank Thee,
For song of bird and hum of bee,
For all things fair we hear or see,
Father in heaven, we thank Thee.

For blue of stream and blue of sky,
    Father, we thank Thee,
For pleasant shade of branches high,
    Father, we thank Thee,
For fragrant air and cooling breeze,
For beauty of the blooming trees,
Father in heaven, we thank Thee.

For this new morning with its light,
    Father, we thank Thee,
For rest and shelter of the night,
    Father, we thank Thee,
For health and food, for love and friends,
For everything Thy goodness sends,
Father in heaven, we thank Thee.

A PSALM

from Psalm One Hundred and Forty-Seven

Sing unto the Lord with thanksgiving;
Sing praise upon the harp unto our God:
Who covereth the heaven with clouds,
Who prepareth rain for the earth,
Who maketh grass to grow upon the mountains,
And herb for the use of men.
He giveth to the beast his food,
And to the young ravens which cry.
Praise the Lord, O Jerusalem;
Praise thy God, O Zion.

SANTA CLAUS

Unknown

Little fairy snowflakes
    Dancing in the flue;
Old Mr. Santa Claus,
    What is keeping you?
Twilight and firelight
    Shadows come and go;
Merry chime of sleighbells
    Twinkling through the snow.
Mother's knitting stockings,
    Pussy's got the ball.

374

Don't you think that Christmas
Is pleasantest of all?

CHRISTMAS

Mother Goose

Christmas comes but once a year,
And when it comes it brings good cheer.

CHRISTMAS IS COMING

Unknown

Christmas is coming
The geese are getting fat

Please to put a penny
In an old man's hat

If you haven't got a penny
A ha'penny will do

If you haven't got a
Ha'penny God bless you!

375

THE FRIENDLY BEAST

French Carol

Jesus, our brother, kind and good
Was humbly born in a stable rude;
The friendly beasts around Him stood,
Jesus, our brother, kind and good.

"I," said the donkey, shaggy and brown,
"I carried His mother up hill and down;
I carried her safely to Bethlehem town.
I," said the donkey, shaggy and brown.

"I," said the cow, all white and red,
"I gave Him my manger for His bed;
I gave Him my hay to pillow His head.
I," said the cow, all white and red.

"I," said the sheep with curly horn,
"I gave Him my wool for a blanket warm;
He wore my coat on Christmas morn.
I," said the sheep with curly horn.

"I," said the camel yellow and black,
"Over the desert upon my back,
I brought Him a gift in the wise man's pack.
I," said the camel yellow and black.

"I," said the dove from the rafters high,
"I cooed Him to sleep so He would not cry,
I cooed Him to sleep, my mate and I.
I," said the dove from the rafters high.

THE BARN

Elizabeth Coatsworth

"I am tired of this barn!" said the colt,
"And every day it snows.
Outside there's no grass any more
And icicles grow on my nose.
I am tired of hearing the cows
Breathing and talking together.
I am sick of these clucking hens.
I *hate* stables and winter weather!"

"Hush, little colt," said the mare,
"And a story I will tell
Of a barn like this one of ours
And the wonders that there befell.
It was weather much like this,
And the beasts stood as we stand now
In the warm good dark of the barn —
A horse and an ass and a cow."

"And sheep?" asked the colt. "Yes, sheep,
And a pig and a goat and a hen.
All of the beasts of the barnyard,
The usual servants of men.
And into their midst came a lady
And she was cold as death,
But the animals leaned above her
And made her warm with their breath.

"There was her Baby born
And laid to sleep in the hay,
While music flooded the rafters
And the barn was as light as day.
And angels and kings and shepherds
Came to worship the Babe from afar,
But we looked at Him first of all creatures
By the bright strange light of a star!"

CRADLE HYMN

Isaac Watts

Hush! my dear, lie still and slumber;
    Holy angels guard thy bed;
Heavenly blessings without number,
    Gently falling on thy head.

How much better thou'rt attended
　　Than the Son of God could be,
When from heaven He descended
　　And became a child like thee!

Soft and easy is thy cradle:
　　Coarse and hard thy Saviour lay,
When His birthplace was a stable,
　　And His softest bed was hay.

See the kindly shepherds round Him,
　　Telling wonders from the sky!
Where they sought Him, there they found Him,
　　With His Virgin Mother by.

See the lovely Babe a-dressing,
　　Lovely Infant, how He smiled,
When He wept, the mother's blessing
　　Soothed and hushed the holy Child.

Lo, He slumbers in the manger,
　　Where the horned oxen fed,
Peace, my darling, here's no danger,
　　Here's no oxen near thy bed.

THE CHRISTMAS CANDLE

Kate Louise Brown

Little taper set tonight,
Throw afar thy tiny light
Up and down the darksome street,
Guide the tender, wandering feet
Of darling Christ-Child sweet.

He is coming in the snow,
As He came so long ago;
When the stars set o'er the hill,
When the town is dark and still,
Comes to do the Father's will.

Little taper, spread thy ray,
Make His pathway light as day;
Let some door be open wide
For this guest of Christmastide,
Dearer than all else beside.

Little Christ-Child, come to me,
Let my heart Thy shelter be;
Such a home Thou wilt not scorn.
So the bells on Christmas morn,
Glad shall ring, "A Christ is born!"

WHY DO THE BELLS OF CHRISTMAS RING

Eugene Field

Why do the bells of Christmas ring?
Why do little children sing?

Once a lovely shining star,
Seen by shepherds from afar,
Gently moved until its light
Made a manger's cradle bright.

There a darling Baby lay
Pillowed soft upon the hay;
And its mother sang and smiled:
"This is Christ, the holy Child!"

Therefore bells for Christmas ring,
Therefore little children sing.

THE FIRST CHRISTMAS

St. Luke 2:8-16

And there were in the same country shepherds abiding in the field, keeping watch over their flock by night.

And lo, the angel of the Lord came upon them, and the glory of the Lord shone round about them: and they were sore afraid.

And the angel said unto them, Fear not: for, behold, I bring you good tidings of great joy, which shall be to all people.

For unto you is born this day in the city of David a Saviour, which is Christ the Lord.

And this shall be a sign unto you; Ye shall find the Babe wrapped in swaddling clothes, lying in a manger.

And suddenly there was with the angel a multitude of the heavenly host praising God, and saying,

Glory to God in the highest, and on earth peace, good will toward men.

And it came to pass, as the angels were gone away from them into heaven, the shepherds said one to another, let us now go even unto Bethlehem, and see this thing which is come to pass, which the Lord hath made known unto us.

And they came with haste, and found Mary, and Joseph, and the Babe lying in a manger.

A CHRISTMAS CAROL

Phillips Brooks

Everywhere, everywhere, Christmas tonight!
Christmas in lands of the fir-tree and pine,

Christmas in lands of the palm-tree and vine,
Christmas where snow-peaks stand solemn and white,
Christmas where corn-fields lie sunny and bright,
Everywhere, everywhere, Christmas tonight!

Christmas where children are hopeful and gay,
Christmas where old men are patient and gray,
Christmas where peace, like a dove in its flight,
Broods o'er brave men in the thick of the fight;
Everywhere, everywhere, Christmas tonight!

For the Christ-child who comes is the Master of all,
No palace too great and no cottage too small,
The angels who welcome Him sing from the height:
"In the city of David, a King in His might."
Everywhere, everywhere, Christmas tonight!

Then let every heart keep its Christmas within,
Christ's pity for sorrow, Christ's hatred of sin,
Christ's care for the weakest, Christ's courage for right,
Christ's dread of the darkness, Christ's love of the light.
Everywhere, everywhere, Christmas tonight!

So the stars of the midnight which compass us round
Shall see a strange glory, and hear a sweet sound,
And cry, "Look! the earth is aflame with delight,
O sons of the morning, rejoice at the sight."
Everywhere, everywhere, Christmas tonight!

Index of Titles

386

387

389

391

393

Index of Authors

402

404

Index of First Lines

409

411

417

419